Heaven Sent, Taylor Made

Cystic Fibrosis
& Transplantation

The Life and Works of Penny Taylor

'Tiger's Clough' picture—painted by Penny while a student at Rivington High School.
This was a place she passed on her way to school, and she wrote a poem about it that
appears later in the book.

'After the Party'—one of Penny's paintings, of a joyful post-party coach ride in Scotland.

First published in Great Britain in 2020 by
Scott Martin Productions
10 Chester Place,
Adlington, Chorley, PR6 9RP

scottmartinproductions@gmail.com
www.scottmartinproductions.com

Contents

Title page and Tiger's Clough painting.

After the Party picture and copyright.

Page 1: Dedication.

Page 2: Why Did I Write This book?

Page 3: A Mother's Story.

Page 7: About Cystic Fibrosis.

Page 10: Physio, Drainage and Ages 3-4.

Page 14: Early School Years and Early Holidays.

Page 20: Special Holidays.

Page 26: High School.

Page 28: Fundraising.

Page 32: Life Goes On, and Awaiting Transplant.

Page 39: Night Journey to Papworth.

Page 45: Faith and Transplant At Last.

Page 57: Whose Heart.

Page 63: Lorraine Kelly and More After Transplant.

Page 68: Thoughts on Transplantation.

Page 71: Post-Transplant.

Page 74: Penny Leaves Us.

Page 80: Sarah Justin.

Page 100: Stephen Thomas.

Page 107: Andrew Burton.

Page 109: Steve Sparkes.

Page 110: Andrew Morley.

Page 115: Mark Burgess.

Page 117: Poems, Letters and Pictures.

Page 152: 'The Babble of Bic'.

Page 160: Appendix.

Page 172: Conclusion.

Page 173: Collage.

Page 175: Judith Would Like to Thank.

Dedication

Dedicated to the memory of our beautiful and loving daughter, Penny

Just before our daughter, Penny, passed away in January 1992, she asked John and I if we would get her work published. This never happened, as we realised at the time how difficult it would be. The sheer amount of memorabilia Penny had accumulated in her short life was astonishing. Not only that, but the emotional aspect was so great that my husband John struggled to go through it. But it was something I wanted and needed to do in order to fulfill Penny's last wish.

With the help of friends like Samantha, Kath, Dorothy, and my husband John (who later came up with the title) the project got started. Then, by chance, I met Lesley, my publisher, and she helped me and drove me on to complete Penny's book.

I would like to thank everyone who has assisted, and also would like to thank all the other people involved throughout Penny's life, for their help, love and support. Without all of you I would not have been able to complete this book,

Judith

Why Did I Write This Book?

John and Judith's wedding day, accompanied by parents.

There are a number of reasons—but mainly I've written 'Heaven Sent, Taylor Made' to tell the story of our daughter, Penny, who suffered from Cystic Fibrosis and became a double-transplantee. Hopefully, within these pages I will show just how faith, a positive outlook, a sense of humour, and family and friends supported her throughout her life.

If someone was to tell you in advance all that is going to happen in your life, your first thought would likely be that there was no way you would cope! Before I married John, I had a breakdown and was in hospital for six months—and it was scary to see other people in hospital with the same condition. When I met John, I vowed that I would tell him about the illness to make him aware of my situation. I told him, and he accepted it. Being very much in love, we got married twelve months after our first meeting.

I came to be expecting a baby two years after our wedding and suffered from a bout of depression while pregnant. The psychiatrist I saw then was a person that I could talk to and trust. He suggested I have a short course of shock treatment and he assured me that no harm would come to the baby or to me.

The church and school that meant so much to Penny and her family.

He was right. So, despite my previous mental health problems I was able to cope with life and eventually was told that I was cured.

Yippee!!!! I was able to enjoy life with my wonderful family, proving that mental health problems can be overcome with the right support from the medical profession, family and friends.

John and I hope that you find much of interest in the pages to come. We also hope that others who find themselves in the same situation can find some strength and hope.

Judith

A young Judith and John Taylor.

A Mother's Story

And now to Penny...

The love and the heartbreak of being a mother who eventually loses her child, started when I became pregnant two years after my marriage to my husband, John.

Penny was born on the 24th of June 1969, at Bolton and District General Hospital, in Farnworth. On the Monday night our friends Dorothy and David called round for a visit. They only lived two doors away and we were all chatting happily when suddenly my waters broke and all hell broke loose. An ambulance arrived and took me to the hospital. John followed, only to be sent home. I was having contractions at that time, but they stopped after a little while, so the sister left me all night until 6am. She then proclaimed that I was suffering from stage fright and announced in a rather stern tone of voice that I was going to have my baby that morning.

Petrified, I was taken to the delivery room and put on a drip. Meanwhile the nurses were dancing around the room to pop music. The drip began its work almost immediately and my unborn child became distressed, so forceps were used to speed up her delivery. Penny arrived at 6:30am weighing 6lb, 3oz.

My first thought was to ask if she was alright and she was—everything seemed perfect. I can remember looking at her and thinking how beautiful she was. John was not allowed to be present at the birth but had called the hospital and had been told that Penny had been born. In John's infinite wisdom, and unbeknown to me, he decided to paint all over our living room windows with the words 'It's a girl. 6lb 3oz' and that we were both doing well. The first time I heard about any of this was when a nurse came to

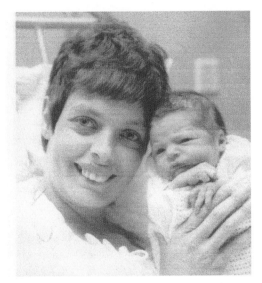

Above: Judith with Penny.

tell me that a reporter from the Bolton Evening News (BEN) wanted to take a photograph of myself and Penny. So, that was how the article about John's painted windows (included above) came to be!

After staying nine days in the hospital following Penny's birth, John arrived to take us home with our mongrel dog, Tramp. The poor dog ignored me when I first got in the car, likely being jealous of the new baby and feeling abandoned by me. We arrived home and settled in, and my sister Barbara arrived from Marple to

Above: Penny's dad, John, who painted her birth announcement on their family home's front window.

lend a hand. Having already had three children of her own she came to show us the ropes. However, Penny was a joy to care for and life was great.

I took Penny to Horwich clinic regularly, and she was seen there by Doctor Sheila McKinley. I enquired as to whether Penny's loose and frequent green stools were normal. She reassured me that this was normal for breast-fed infants at first.

But her stools did not alter, and after eleven weeks my mother asked our general practitioner Doctor Kneafsey to do something, and so Penny was admitted back to Bolton District Hospital—the first of her many hospital visits. After being admitted and examined, the doctors felt the cause of Penny's loose stools was likely to be gastroenteritis. So, I was told to wean Penny off the breast as they needed her to accept a bottle for fluids which she did not take kindly to!

At this time, John and I were both inexperienced in hospital ways, and although Penny was under the care of a paediatrician called Dr Dickson, we hadn't seen or spoken to him in the two weeks that Penny had been under his care— and Penny didn't appear to be improving.

Penny was now taking bottled milk called SMA, and it didn't seem to be making any difference. But one day the ward sister told us that Penny was much better and that we should bring her clothes for her return home the following day.

Dr Dickson came in to see us shortly afterwards and told us that Penny wouldn't be going home that day. This was the first time we had spoken to Dr Dickson, though we'd seen him on the wards.

Unknown to us, he'd had a sweat test carried out on Penny. We were devastated to hear that the results were positive—our daughter had Cystic Fibrosis, an incurable genetic disease affecting the lungs and digestive system.

We came out of Dr Dickson's office and went straight up to my mother and father's house at Nook Farm, Harwood, to break the news that our first-born child had an incurable disease. Like us, they were unprepared and hadn't expected something so serious to be wrong with Penny. From there we went to tell John's mum and dad at Chorley New Road, and they were also devastated.

Looking back now it feels almost as if what we found out that day had been told to someone else, and not to us at all. It was so long ago, and when I say that, it sometimes feels that after all we went through since then a thousand years have passed.

At the time we were told about Penny's Cystic Fibrosis,

Above: Penny with Judith, and with John.

Below: Doctor Walter Dickson.

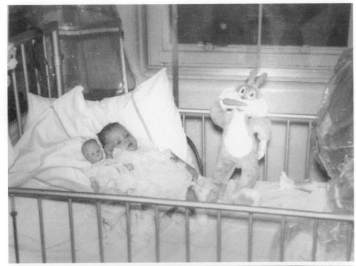

Above: Penny in hospital with just some of her beloved furry friends and on a photoshoot with a doll.
Below Left: At six months old in hospital.
Below Right: Baby Penny with furry toys. Judith still has the small teddy and large panda called Little Penny from Penny's first Christmas.

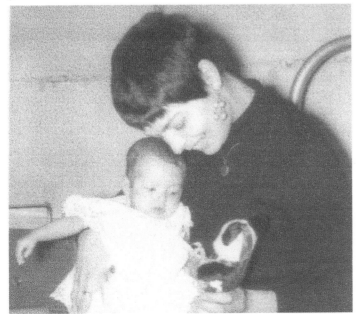

we had never heard about this condition and were horrified about what it might mean for Penny's future.

The days that followed were filled with fear and trepidation about what we were all about to face. Our first reaction was a need to meet another child with Cystic Fibrosis and to hear about the condition from their parents, and that's one of the reasons why I've written this book.

During this post-diagnosis time, I wept and experienced a mixture of many feelings. Would we cope? Was Penny going to live?

I went over so many things in my mind—would she have a normal life? What quality of life would she have? I was overcome with sadness and felt completely numb.

I thought John and I would grow closer as a result of our shared sadness, yet we both tried to protect each other from our own feelings. I can only think we did this out of fear of letting the other feel we were weak. I tried to be strong, although I needed to talk about the situation more than John felt he could or wanted to. I also felt lonely and out of touch because I couldn't say what I wanted to at the time I wanted to say it.

As others in similar situations might have experienced, I was also conscious of the fact that I couldn't talk to just anyone about it, and was nervous of boring people with my need to express how I felt.

Everything had changed overnight—it felt as if all our hopes and dreams had to be abandoned, but in fact they just changed to take into account how Cystic Fibrosis would affect our lives.

Four of Penny's pieces of art. She loved to draw and paint, and she loved her teddies too. Many of her other pictures are included in this book.

About Cystic Fibrosis

Between one in twenty and one in twenty-five people are carriers of the Cystic Fibrosis gene. Carriers experience no ill effects, but if two carriers have children, each child they conceive would have a one in four chance of having Cystic Fibrosis, a two in four chance of being a carrier, and a one in four chance of being free of the Cystic Fibrosis gene. This makes it the most common recessive genetic disease amongst Europeans.

Being born with the disease Muco-viscidosis (or Cystic Fibrosis as we know it in the United Kingdom) has startling effects on what appears to be a normal child.

The most important feature is that mucus produced by a CF sufferer is far more viscous (thicker) than that of a non-CF sufferer. This thicker mucus results in problems with lungs and bowels. The bowels are affected by digestive problems meaning that the patient needs to take an enzyme capsule with every meal.

The problem with the lungs is much more serious. It must be understood that mucus is produced in the lungs as a cleaning agent. It is constantly gathering up bacteria and flushing them out of the lungs. But, as you can imagine, if the mucus is more viscous than normal, instead of flushing the lungs out to clean them, the mucus, along with the collected bacteria, becomes lodged in the lungs and creates pockets of intense infection. This is a very brief and simplified explanation of the disease.

Penny with her dad and childhood friend, John Duckworth.

Penny, and some of her soft toys. Bumbum, the toy on Penny's knee, was won at a tombola, and, together with Tiny Ted, was with her all her life.

In the 1960s, children were diagnosed with this disorder by means of the sweat test. It is still used to this day. It is used because the sweat of all Cystic Fibrosis sufferers is four times more salty than that of a non-sufferer. So measuring the relative salt content in the sweat gives a clear indication about whether or not the patient has Cystic Fibrosis.

WHEN CYSTIC FIBROSIS KILLS.

When dies a friend, so suddenly —
A friend who's shared your fears,
And witnessed all the highs and lows —
You cannot stop the tears.
They flow with such abundancy,
And fall within your heart.
It's hard to say that last 'Goodbye',
Where life and death do part.
We're all the same, us cystic folk;
We fight to breathe and walk.
And though no two are quite alike,
We all know how to talk!
We talk within the wards at night
As though there's no tomorrow!
But sadly, for some, there's just tonight —
No dawn; no light; no morrow.
This year has been a dreadful time —
I've lost so many a friend!
They were merely folk like you, or I,
Hoping that life won't end.
For twenty years — or twenty five —
Became a struggle to stay alive,
And under thirty is no age
To reach lifes final, dying stage.
And all they asked for was the chance
To build their hopes! Their dreams, to dance!
Just lifes rich pattern to enhance!
A transplant was their only hope —
Their last surviving dream!
But as the donors were lacking so,
Their time ran out, it seems.

I'm left to fight, and breathe, and hope —
Along with many others.
Though I hate to keep 'farewelling' folk
More loyal to me than brothers.

Who laughed with them? Who cuddled them?
Who cared to understand?
I pray they all had someone
To reassure, and hold their hand.

Yes, I wait. And hope. And pray the same —
Though I don't WANT folk to die.
But if their death, a life could save —
There would only be one 'Goodbye'.
So to all my friends who cling, and hope,
Stay optimistic! Never mope!
And to all who lost — those friends I knew —
Farewell, brave ones! Goodbye! Adieu!

Penny Taylor.
2. November. 89.

Penny Taylor age 7½

Neigh ... I'm racy about you.

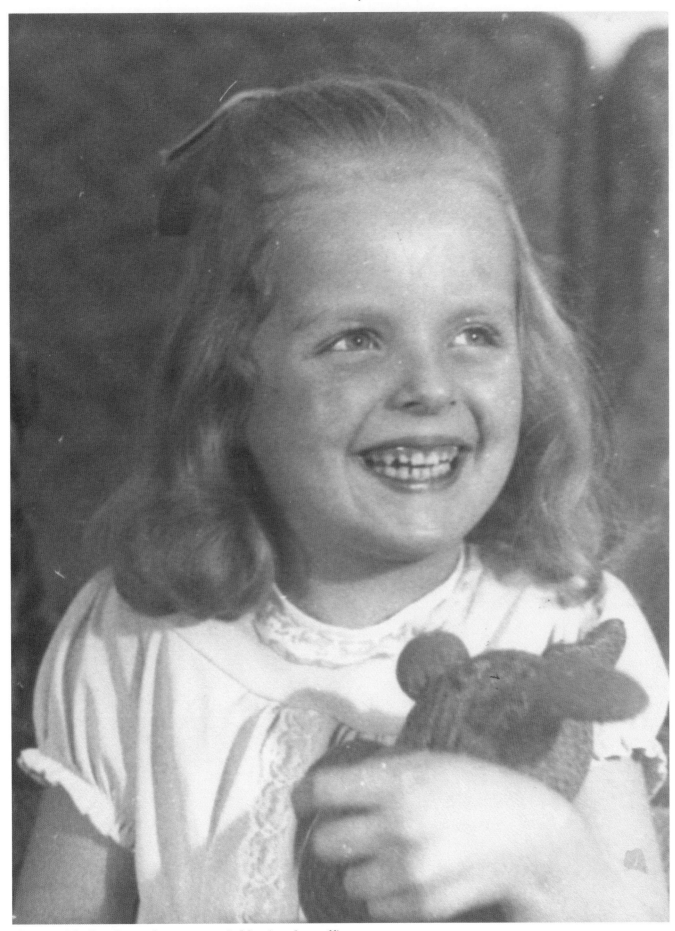

Penny with Bumbum who accompanied her into her coffin.

Physio and Postural Drainage

Life continued, and Penny went from strength to strength. Her first birthday came and went. Penny continued to attend regular hospital appointments for checkups, but also went to Bolton Royal Infirmary for regular physiotherapy sessions.

That was when we saw Mrs Hastings who first taught us both how to carry out postural drainage (PD) on Penny. Penny would be tipped over a few pillows with her head sloping downwards lower than the rest of her body. We were taught how to pat her back with cupped hands and how hard we could do this without hurting her. We learnt how to squeeze her ribs together and gently shake the top half of her torso. Afterwards we sat her up and she would dribble out any sputum brought up by the drainage. This procedure had to be done at least four times a day. At times when the lungs became infected, a nebuliser would also be used to help loosen sputum. As time went on and Penny grew older, she was taught how to bring the sputum up herself through coughing and breathing exercises.

Sputum is a very sticky substance which attaches itself to all the small hairs in the throat and down inside the lungs. The colour of the sputum varies. It could be white, yellow or grey, and every so often a sample was sent to pathology labs to be tested for infections. The sample would be grown on a culture and tested to see what infections was present. Then appropriate antibiotics would be given if necessary.

While Penny was going every week to see Mrs Hastings and Miss Jolly, it was suggested that another little girl join Penny in her sessions, as she was upset by all the procedures. This enabled her to see how well Penny tolerated her PD. Gradually she began to improve, but Penny decided to start playing up. It was as if they had swapped roles for a time.

A trampoline was provided by the hospital to allow Penny to jump up and down—something that kept the sputum loose. It was an enormous thing and lived in the dining room for a time, but it was a struggle walking round it to get up the stairs. So, eventually it was moved into the garage where all the children liked to play on it. John and I also bought Penny a rocking horse which played its own part in helping to keep the sputum loose.

Penny with her dad John, Michele, Lesley and her brother Tony in Bull's Brow (known by locals as Bull's Brew) behind Penny's school.

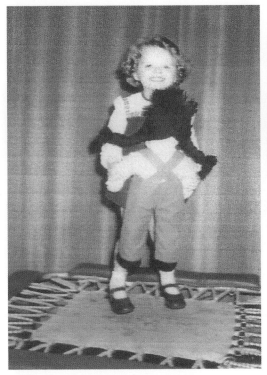

Penny and ragdoll Jemima on the trampoline, and on the rest of the page, on many sets of wheels!

UNFENCED RICHES.

I once saw a Rainbow in the sky;

It really was way up high,

But I never saw the pot of Gold;

For it is there, or so I'm told.

Before School

At age three, Penny started playschool at Fox Street with her little friends, John Duckworth and Lesley Harrison. John's mum, Kath, and I were friends from our hairdressing days, and we would often meet up when dropping the children off. Now Penny was mixing with a larger number of children, I worried at the higher risk of Penny picking up infections.

Penny, John and Lesley played well together, especially painting and colouring—and Penny also really enjoyed mixing with the other children.

Penny also started to regularly attend Sunday school with Lesley who lived in one of the houses directly across from our back gate. Pat Harrison and I would take it in turns to walk the pair up to Sunday school. They would come home with drawings and stamps. Penny used to keep her stamps and put them in a book. Collecting was an important hobby for Penny, right from being a toddler to being an adult. You name it, Penny collected it—sugar packets, straws, feathers, pebbles—anything and everything—just like her dad.

Penny was a lively child and many a happy hour was spent in the courtyard at the back of our house, playing games with Lesley. They would make dens from a clothes maiden with a sheet draped over the top. Dolls in prams were taken out for walks and Tramp the dog was included in all the games too. Lesley and Penny were as thick as thieves and were always popping in and out of each others' houses. They laughed a lot and were very giddy together. Eventually they became known as the terrible twins.

Penny and John Duckworth.

Top: Two favourite photos of Penny and Lesley. Middle: Penny and Tramp. Bottom: Penny and fuchsias.

Four Years

For Penny's fourth birthday we held a party in the garage. Penny's cousins came from Marple and friends came from near and far. The children played outside in the courtyard on bikes and space hoppers. It was a sunny day and it was lovely to watch them all playing. We had set a table up in the garage for the food—sandwiches, jelly, cake and lots of other party goodies.

Penny wore one of her short-sleeved dresses. It was blue and trimmed with yellow, and it had a sailor collar. I thought Penny looked beautiful—her hair was curly and blonde, and she always had a cheeky smile. Penny's Auntie Margaret used to make most of Penny's clothes out of pretty material, and I would have liked to have dressed Penny in one of these for her party. However, every year for her birthday, Bessie, a friend of Penny's granny, would make her a dress especially for the occasion. Bessie would mention in passing that she would pop round on Penny's birthday to see her in the new dress. It was lovely of Bessie to go to so much trouble, though I then always felt obliged to put Penny in the dresses Bessie had made.

Anyway, the fourth birthday party went well, and fun was had by all.

Penny's Early School Years

A few months after her fourth birthday, Penny started school at Horwich Parish Church of England School on Church Street, just opposite where we live. You could probably throw a stone from one of our upstairs windows on to the school grounds. The first day Pat and I took Penny and her daughter Lesley to the school I'm sure that Pat felt the same depth of emotion as I was feeling. We were both seeing our little ones grow up and start school—it had all happened so quickly as if in the blink of an eye. We both returned home and wept!

But the girls loved their first day at school and came back with lots of tales to tell us. The Head Teacher, Ron Sutcliffe, and the other teachers were all aware of Penny's Cystic Fibrosis and how it affected her. At this stage Penny still went to the hospital once a month, and more often if she was experiencing other problems.

Penny enjoyed primary school and also started piano lessons with Mrs Baron, who would beat time with a little stick. Penny was a keen musician and happily settled into the routine of practicing for an hour a day. I decided that I would also like to learn to play the piano and eventually I too went along to Mrs Baron's house for lessons. So poor John had to not only listen to Penny's practice sessions, but also to the sound of me practicing my scales!

The piano was in our living room for Penny's entire life and brought her much pleasure when she was ill and unable to go out. She took piano exams whilst at primary school and still studying with Mrs Baron.

Art was also a love of hers, even at this young age, and this was a skill that she developed throughout her life—perhaps she inherited this from her dad who was also very keen on painting and had been to Art College.

Penny would attend Sunday School with her friend Lesley but neither John nor I went to church. One day Penny asked, 'How is it you get me dressed up to go to Sunday School and you two don't go to church?' She had a point there! A few years later we did both begin to attend church each Sunday. Penny had a Christian faith from being quite young and that faith became more important with each coming year.

Penny had her first serious infection at four years old, and the District Nurse would visit daily to give her an injection.

Above: Penny and Michele on the way to the Isle of Man.

Below: Penny and Michele on the sofa at Granny Taylor's.

However, as soon as Penny heard the doorbell she would hide upstairs and refuse to come down! She didn't win the battle of the injections!

When Penny was six years old her Grandma Hilton died. Up till then she'd really enjoyed the time spent with her grandparents. At around this time, she was also a bridesmaid for her Auntie Linda and Uncle David.

At eight years old Penny was given a dolls' house for her birthday and this became a great joy for her. She always made sure that it was tidy and in order whenever her Auntie Margaret and her daughter Deborah came to visit, as Margaret would always check that everything was in order and that furniture was in the correct location!

Penny took part in Sports' Days at school and also loved to cycle. This was a love that never left her—she even went on a family biking holiday after her transplant.

At the age of nine, Penny had her first intravenous treatment for infection. This was a treatment that would be repeated many times throughout her life, and her friend Michele visited her daily throughout the process. Theirs was to be a friendship that lasted all Penny's life.

Penny's Granddad Hilton died at this time and this was very distressing for Penny as they were extremely close.

Following her IV treatment at age nine we were all able to go on holiday to Dubrovnik which was a great boost for Penny after the distress of losing her granddad.

Bridesmaid Penny at the wedding of Auntie Linda and Uncle David.

Penny and Lesley on their primary school's steps.

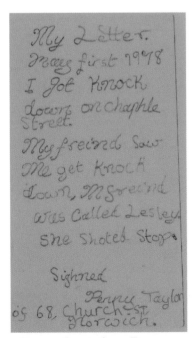

Above: A note from Penny written after a road accident.

Penny and Deborah on holiday.

Penny and Her Love of Music

♪♪ HAPPY BIRTHDAY
FOR YESTERDAY.

15th August 1988.

Dear Mrs Baron,
          I thought I would write you a little letter seeing as I am unable to come to see you. I rang Eileen and was pleased to hear that you were on your feet again. I'm sure they'll have you home again in no time.

Now a lot has happened since I saw you last week so I don't really know where to begin. I wasn't too pleased with this dry weather we had - as a result I became dehydrated. This played havoc with my chest and on Thursday I went to see the Dr. at Monsall. I took my friend Michelle with me for "moral support" as I had a nasty feeling that I would be put back on the intravenous treatment. As you can imagine, it was a huge relief when the Dr. put me on tablets instead. Afterall, what difference will a few more pills make. I'm now on 47 a day! I was glad of course when the damp weather returned:-
... and I've decided that the foreign countries can keep their hot weather to themselves.

On Thursday night Michele and I were sat having our tea and a gossip when the phone rang. It was my friend Stephen from Fleetwood ringing to see if he could come over on the train on Friday. I met him whilst I was in hospital in December. He also has CF. We have a lot in common as he is also an Art Student allthough he has only been at college for a year. He use to work but, when he was 24, he decided that a little more education wouldn't do any harm and he's hoping, one day, to teach art. At the moment he's doing the 2nd year of a 2 year fine Art course and on Thursday he'll find out whether he's passed his A level pottery.

He arrived in Horwich at 9.30 am on Friday. I don't think I've ever got ready as quick in my life. We picked him up from Blackrod Station, he is ever so brown. Now we know where the sun is !! Incidently, do you

Penny loved her piano lessons. Her teacher, Mrs Baron, became a good friend to Penny, and Penny wrote to her when Mrs Baron was ill. When Penny was twelve, Mrs Baron also took Judith on as a pupil!

remember the fish van from Fleetwood, say about 10 yrs ago, that used to come over to Horwich? Stephens Dad used to drive that van. Funny isn't it !!

However, I don't think it was the same one that you knew. This one went to the Loco works. Still, it could have been.

We took him to have a look at the two Barns up Rivington, he seemed quite impressed. Unfortunately, it was raining (and I mean RAINING!) so it was too wet for us to go a walk around the grounds which are next to the Barns. We already sounded like a couple of old bellows but it was nice to talk to someone in the same boat who understood what it was like to get breathless talking. We had dinner at "The Jolly Crofters", both ordering chicken + chips. It was really crowded and we moved seats 3 times before we found somewhere we could sit, chat, and hear each other. We had a few slight problems with GRAMMAR. For instance, he didn't know that "gab" and "gas" meant "talk", so there were a few instances when we had to explain what we we were talking about.

However. We got by!

In the afternoon we went to Wigan Pier, yes, at Wigan!! He was quite amazed by it all and he especially liked the coal mine scenery. We spent ages going backwards and forwards through it. The dummys weren't very realistic though. I had to laugh though when, on seeing two people sat in wheelchairs, Stephen thought they too were dummies and was about to go and have a look at them.

When we had finished looking around the exhibits we had a ride on the boat there which takes you to another part of the pier. In this part they keep the engines which use to power the factory. It was steam driven and was quite amazing to watch. A huge wheel was turned by pistons and things which in turn powers the other machines. Its fascinating. But it got extremely hot so we were glad to get

outside again. We then caught the boat back and met up with Mum and her friend Norma.

At night we all took him back to Fleetwood in the car. We, both exhausted as we had talked and giggled all day nonstop.

This Wednesday my friend Michele is coming over from Daffcocker. She had a baby boy, Ryan, in March so she's going to bring him over and we're taking him down to Gran & Grandads. Michele use to live next door to them so they're looking forward to seeing Ryan. He's a big baby though. He weighed 9lb 11oz when he was born. Quite a heavy-weight.

Well, I'll away the noo! I hope you enjoy reading this letter. Hurry up and get well soon! I'll get my music at the ready and bring it down as soon as you arrive home.

Keep Cheery!

A big lick from Freeway!

Love from Mum + Dad too!

Lots of love
Penny. xxx
X

Above: Penny's felt tip drawing of Teddy and Bumbum—two of her much-loved companions.

Penny in the Brownies

Below: A letter from ten year old Penny to her parents while she was away on a Brownie trip to Waddow Hall in June 1980.
Right: Brownies on parade and at camp.

I think its 30th June (80)

Dear Mum and Dad,
                    We got here at about 1.30 p.m. and waited for a Land Rover to take the Rucksacks to the piece of land we are on, the land is called Canada. We pitched up the tent and then we had a drink. Later we had Potatoe mash (yummy) and beetroot and a drink of water. Before we had our tea we had a duty to do. There are water, cook, orderly, health, and wood, we had to do water (ugh) we had to walk quite a long way ~~long way~~ quite a long way we had to carry buckets about that full 🥣. All of a sudden a Bull and some Cows chased Caroline and me, (well that what we thought anyway but they where really going to the trough) so when we got to the dustbin which we had to fill there was about that much → 🅰.

we had to make a wash bowl after tea like this → 🅰 with a draning board → 🖭. Later we went to bed at 10.00 and Silence at 10.30, (well not in. our tent was Silence) P.S. Caroline got the basin for a wash and forgot to take it back and I borrowed it as well even though Id done my ~~teeth~~ I had a wash and caroline went to bed with the rest of forgeting about the wash basin so I had to get up and walk round the tent with nothing on my feet and but my wellies on and take the basin back, and it was dark. Later in the week we are hoping to go on a walk. MONDAY- look round the shop. Thursday- Baths. I've remembered my tablets. The Toilets STINK Terrible. Today we had Tomatoes, fried bread, bacon, and Cornflakes. After we washed up and ~~had~~ we had to do a duty - Health (1.) Tidy wash cubicles and lavs. (2) Put out clean hand ~~towels~~ towels (didn't do) (3) Change grease trap. (4) Burn the incinerator. (5) Bash Flat all tins. We had dinner and washed up. Last night a tent fell down. We have a mug line. The patrols are THUMPER, Dennis the Menace, Bumble, Snoopy and Minnie Mouse.

We have made a luggage rack. I've just had my dinner. SEE You Soon. Lots of love from Penny. xxx P.S weather is fine up to now.

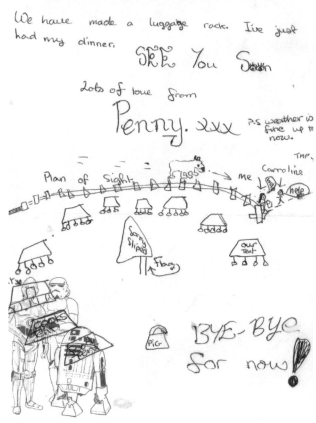

Early Holidays

Camping in Carlyon Bay was one of the best family holidays we ever had.

It wasn't long before Penny's health began to improve and we even went on holiday.

We returned home, and Penny was suntanned and looking quite healthy. We felt as if we'd achieved something special that we thought would never have been possible a short time earlier. We had holidays at Carlyon Bay and Menabily a year later, and John dropped his camera in the sea. Penny found it hilarious and I'm sure she thought he'd done it specially for her own amusement. This was one of our most memorable treasured holidays and one we thought we'd never be able to have.

Other holidays that we enjoyed were in caravans which were owned by the CF Trust to enable CF children and their family members to have a holiday. We went to Caister-on-Sea, Bingley in Yorkshire with Debbie and a chalet in Isle of Man with Michele. We took one of Penny's friends with us on each holiday.

We had to use a space age pram (above right) while camping in Cornwall. It was necessary to bring along a humidifying tent which we put up in a barn. The rest of the time Penny needed to be inside this smaller tent which was fixed to the pram.

All this is proof that Cystic Fibrosis doesn't necessarily stop families from doing things together. You just need a big car! I still have no recollection of how we managed to fit everything into and on top of our VW Beetle back then!

Judith's mum, John, Tramp, Penny, Judith and Judith's dad at Southport.

Top to Bottom: Penny in her space age pram. With her dad, John. Playing on a towel next to the sea, With her mum and dog on a rocky beach.

January/February 1980—Our Special Holidays

Disneyland and New Zealand

22nd January 1980 marked the start of one of the most exciting holidays we ever had. We asked Penny's paediatrician, Dr Dickson, what he thought about us taking the holiday as Penny wasn't too well at the time.

He replied 'Go for it,' so we did.

The flight to Los Angeles was long and very tiring. We checked in at our hotel, 'The Sheraton'. The following day we went to Disneyland, which was quite magical, especially watching Penny's face as she met Tigger and the other Disney characters. The following day we went to Hollywood and Universal Studios. We did all the things that folk do in these places and had a wonderful time.

That evening we left the city on a flight to Auckland, New Zealand. Shortly after we boarded the plane, we asked if it would be possible to visit the flight deck. The Purser said that he would try to arrange it later as they were very busy at the start of the flight. But later, he asked if we would like to come to the flight deck. He asked Penny if she believed in fairy stories, then told her a story

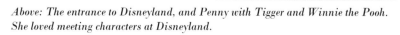
Above: The entrance to Disneyland, and Penny with Tigger and Winnie the Pooh. She loved meeting characters at Disneyland.

about an express train, and pressed a button. A noise came on which sounded like a train going past, and another button he pressed sounded like 'Cock a Doodle Doo'. Penny thanked him and went off to join the junior jet club and acquire a great many souvenirs to add to her collection.

We flew on to Honolulu to change crew, and then on to Auckland. From there we got another flight to Christchurch. Our friend, Ken, was there to greet us with a bunch of flowers and a beaming smile and he then took us back to his Christchurch home. We were the first people from the UK to have visited him since he had emigrated.

Ken was good enough to let us use his car while we were there which meant that we could visit many places in the South Island. The first place we visited was Akarua on Banks Peninsula. While there we met a lovely lady called Margaret Lacy who took us back to her

Above: Ken and John with teddy, Bumbum and Mickey Mouse in New Zealand.

Left: Ken and John during a visit to Penny's house in Horwich. Ken and John were scouts together and lifelong friends.

Penny in a New Zealand cable car and on a boat in New Zealand.

house for a cup of tea, and Penny had some home-made blackcurrant juice which she loved. Margaret also had a cat called Cinderella.

We went away for a few days with Ken and stayed at a school outdoor lodge on the west side of Arthur's Pass, called Kokiri Lodge. From there we went gold panning at Blue Spur Gold Mine, and Penny got herself some real gold dust! From there we went to Greymouth and Shanty Town, we had a ride on an old train through the bush, and followed it all by picnicking with Ken's friends, Peggy and Russell.

On then to Punakaiki and the Pancake Rocks and blow holes which were fascinating. Then we plunged into the Tasman Sea.

We packed and returned to Christchurch, John and Penny filled out their diaries and then the following day Ken went to work and we set off on our journey. We went south through Ashburton, Lake Tekapo, and encountered the Church of the Good Shepherd, where a statue of a border collie dog had been created, in memory of all the dogs that had opened up the country. We went through a place called Twizel, had a meal, got some cash and made our way to Mount Cook where we booked in at a youth hostel. Then we had a ride to the Tasman

Margaret Lacy, Penny and John on grass near a river in Ribchester. Margaret was from Akarua on South Island, NZ. We met her there, went for cuppa, stayed in touch, and later we invited her to the UK, but she insisted on saving up to come first class!

Above: Judith, Margaret, Penny and Kathryn. They picked us up from Wellington airport.

Glacier which becomes a river of 29km long. It was getting late and very cold, so that night we all slept with our clothes on.

The next day it was so cold at Mount Cook and Penny wasn't very well so, although it was a carless day, we decided to take a risk and drive down to Twizel where we stayed in a log cabin. We went on from there to Cromwell, and then on to Queenstown. Penny saw a doctor there who confirmed that she had tonsillitis. We went to the North Island after that. Before we'd left home we'd discovered we had relations there and had arranged to meet them in Wellington.

We travelled there across Cook Strait, then cousin Margaret picked us up and took us to her

Above: Penny at the Air New Zealand sign, pointing at London.

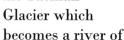

Above : Mount Cook

daughter, Kathryn. By that point we were running out of money so they looked after us back at their house in Fielding and took us round Rotorua and other places, then ran us to Auckland Airport so we could make our way to Singapore.

Above: Ken, Penny and Judith gold panning in New Zealand's South Island.

Above: Christchurch, New Zealand.

Right: John and Penny at the mud geysers.

Below: Letters home from New Zealand and other times away. Penny took work with her on her long holiday and kept in touch with school.

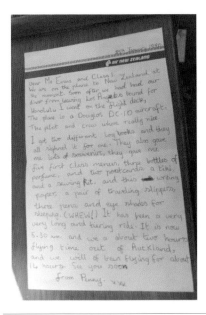

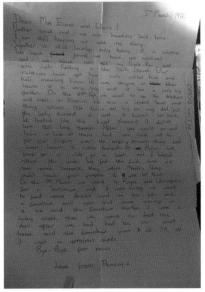

23

Heaven Sent, Taylor Made

Left Top: Our New Zealand relatives, Warwyck, Royce and their children.

Left Bottom: Ken, Judith and Penny.

Right Top: Warwyck's mum and dad, Margaret and Bill.

Right Bottom: John in the snow on return to Horwich.

Singapore

It was so hot in Singapore and I couldn't cope with the heat, though Penny and John did. But we did all manage to go to a show and to a garden where Penny stood under a massive orchid plant. Penny also had a rickshaw ride!

Coming back home, we had too much luggage and the airline wanted far too much money for us to take it as excess baggage.

We were reluctant to let go of any of our treasures, but eventually we were allowed onto the almost-empty plane, with all our luggage!

Astonishingly, when we returned from Singapore, it was snowing!

Three pictures from Singapore: A typical Singapore building, Penny on a rickshaw bike and standing under an orchid plant.

Holidays in Scotland

Alan, David and Ian (sons of Auntie Betty and Uncle Dave.

Above: Strathtummel post office in Scotland, an extraordinarily small looking building.

Ever since my childhood I have gone to Scotland during the school holidays. I usually stayed at Auntie Betty's in Dumfries. She was married to Uncle Dave who had three sons, Alan, Ian and David, all of whom I used to play with. Dave had three brothers – Bill, Jock (John) and Bert. Bill and his family lived in Glasgow and their son Roy would also come to Auntie Betty's for holidays. We also stayed with Uncle Bert and his wife Auntie Ann in various parts of Scotland, as they were always moving house. My other Auntie Betty McBurnie, and Uncle Bill, lived in Glasgow!

As their families grew up and got married, Dave's eldest son, Alan, married Joan and they had the twins, Jane and Alan. In their teenage years, Penny and young Alan started writing to one another and built up a strong friendship. They shared the same kind of humour and got on really well. They even named a wood near to where Alan lived 'Alpen' (Alan and Penny). This was a wood about which Penny wrote a book, and they referred to themselves as the King and Queen of Alpen when they wrote to one another. You can see examples of some of their correspondence elsewhere in the book.

We also had lovely holidays in Glasgow at cousin Roy and Anne's. They have a daughter, Veronica, and a son, Robin. They also have families now, but Veronica wrote to Penny till she died. Veronica was training to be a doctor and took Penny round the university. During one of these visits, Penny saw much that inspired her poetry writing.

We all spent happy times with them, and Penny stayed there while she participated in the Transplant Games in Glasgow.

Above: A family party for Auntie Betty in Scotland.

Come fly with me!

Left: Roy's mum (Auntie Betty) used to bring my cousin Roy down to our farm when we were young. We went up there too. The photo is of Anne, Robin, Better (who was married to Uncle Bill), Veronica and Roy (my cousin).

Penny at High School

When Penny started Rivington High School she looked so grown up in her uniform—how quickly the years had gone! As much as was possible, we had always treated her like any other child, but if she was off-colour we would drive her to school in the car. She preferred to walk to school with her friends, but this was not always possible. When John got a motorbike, Penny enjoyed riding pillion and at this time she also enjoyed going to disco parties at the church and to her friends' parties and outings. She had been a Brownie in the Horwich Parish Church Brownie Pack and then progressed into the Girl Guides section as she got older.

When Penny was twelve, she went on an exchange visit to France organised by her school. Unfortunately, she once again got an infection whilst in France and had to go to the local hospital for x-rays and antibiotic treatment. As you can imagine, it was very difficult knowing that our daughter was ill and so far away, but fortunately the family that she was staying with sounded

Megan, Penny and Sarah, high school friends.

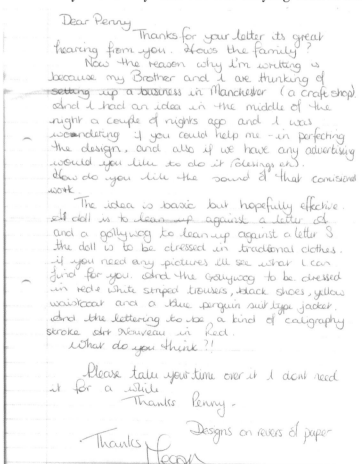

A letter from Megan, years after high school.

very sensible and caring when they phoned us, so we were reassured. They'd even arranged a birthday party for her which was a very kind gesture.

In turn, Natasha from the French family came to stay with us and, as neither John nor I spoke any French, communication was difficult. When she said 'eau' we thought she was saying 'oh! But she actually wanted water!

The school arranged a dance at Rivington Barn for all the

students—but Natasha decided to go walkabout with a boy, and this caused the teachers a frantic few minutes. It also left us cautious whenever we went out with her as we didn't want a repeat performance.

Freeway, our mongrel dog who was part Skye Terrier and part Bearded Collie, came into our lives and was the love of Penny's life. She took him out for walks, which was very beneficial to her health.

Penny was now enjoying good health and was able to do all the things her friends were doing.

Above Right: A painting of Penny's from 1987, perhaps inspired by the trees and plants around Penny's high school, Rivington and Blackrod (Above Left).

Left: Penny with Dr Shuba Panja. Doctor Panja became Penny's GP when Penny was in her late teens, and she cared for her all through the transplant process. She was with Penny right up to the end.

Above: Deborah and Penny at Deborah's birthday, and Right: Penny on her bike, with Freeway looking on.

Fundraising

In 1970, when Penny was just eight months old, her Consultant, Dr Dickson, had suggested that we might like to join the Bolton Branch of the Cystic Fibrosis Research Trust. By Penny's later childhood and adolescence we'd become involved in fundraising and Penny was an enthusiastic part of this. We held flag days where people would dress in fancy dress costumes such as clowns, Sylvester the Cat or Bugs Bunny, and children would be given balloons on sticks. We also held street collections often dressed in period costumes.

Jumble sales and sponsored walks also helped to raise funds and Penny, Dave Burgess and his son, Mark, took part in a carnival Fun Run which was a remarkable feat for both Penny and Mark, who was also a CF sufferer.

We held a Ball at The Last Drop Village—local restaurant and hotel. Famous DJ, Alan Freeman, compered the event and kindly donated his services for free. Local shops donated prizes for a tombola stall and the ball raised £1000. Penny was well enough to participate in all these activities and enjoyed raising the profile of CF.

In 1985 Penny took part in another Fun Run and was photographed by the Bolton Evening News as she neared our house at the end of her run.

In a third Fun Run the day was quite windy and a very kind lady said to Penny, 'You run behind me, love, and I'll keep the wind off you!'

Judith, Michele, a representative from the Rotary Club, John, Penny, John's cousin Linda, and Jackie (Judith's friend) at a 1985 fundraiser that was one of the last proper fundraiser events for Cystic Fibrosis, Bolton.

Message Of Hope

Horwich girl Penny Taylor's completion of the Horwich Carnival Fun Run course was not only a reflection of her own personal courage, but also a defiant message of hope for all sufferers of Cystic Fibrosis.

When Penny was born with the disease, her parents were told she would probably die in infancy and certainly die before her early teens.

Now, she is 16, a member of Bolton Arts Circle, Bolton Church Group, and the Church Youth Fellowship Association and has competed in the Carnival race three times in the last four years.

Penny, who hopes to have raised over £58 for the Cystic Fibrosis Trust with her 57 minute run, told the Trader, "The disease doesn't affect me as badly as it does some people. I had to walk a bit then run, but at least I got round."

FRIENDS

Three of Penny's friends, Sarah Whatmough, and Karen and Nicholas Gee, ran with her, raising another £85 between them to help Cystic Fibrosis research which is now reported to be nearer than ever to a crucial breakthrough.

Horwich Carnival Fun Run Race Organiser, Maureen Unsworth said, "It's due to people like Penny that the Run is such a great success, simply because the sight of her encourages more fortunate people to take part every year."

Penny is currently studying for her "A" levels at Rivington and Blackrod High School, and determinedly commented, "You've never got to give up hope, and keep fighting, and enjoy life to the full. I just take each day as it comes."

● *Penny Taylor proudly displaying her Horwich Carnival Fun Run medal.*

Photo above: Back row—Judith, niece Catherine, John and Stan (under the lamp!). Front row—Barbara (Judith's sister), Helen (Judith's niece), John (Judith's nephew) and John's wife Helen. Penny at front. This was taken one day when we went for a meal and spent some time with the family

Left and Above Left: All dressed up for a fundraiser at Bolton's Victorian market. John Taylor, friend Lorraine Rosekilly, John's Auntie Ruth, his cousin Linda, Judith Taylor and Sandra.

Above: John Taylor (in dress) with Martin Rosekilly on a fundraising mission.

PRETTY PENNY'S A RUNNING MARVEL!

By ALAN KAY

PRETTY teenager Penny Taylor's performance in Sunday's Horwich Carnival Fun Run is unimportant.

For her mere appearance on the starting line is symbolic of her success against a serious illness.

When Penny was born her father, John, announced the news by daubing it in paint on the front window of his home in Church Street, Horwich.

But a few months later, his jubilation turned to sadness when it was found that Penny suffered from cystic fibrosis.

The disease threatens the lives of thousands of children, and John and his wife Judith were told that Penny could die. But with careful treatment she became one of many sufferers who now emerged from childhood with fairly good health.

CHAMPIONS

Penny's life has been a marathon of hospital visits, physiotherapy, and bouts of respiratory infection to which the disease made her prone.

But her parents are champions of the struggle to increase public understanding and to calm the worst fears of parents of other sufferers.

They help run the Bolton branch of the CF's Research Trust, a fund raising and advice giving organisation.

And Penny, a 15-years-old Rivington High School pupil, is proof that the disease can be contained and need not always be a barrier to an active life.

John, aged 44, said: "Penny was desperately ill as a baby, but with good management and good treatment she is now achieving things that we never thought were possible."

WARY

There is still no cure for the disease and Penny has treatment daily, but much of it she administers herself which allows her independence.

However, she still has to be wary of cold and wet weather and is hoping for some sunshine on Sunday.

● The five mile fun run starts at 1.30 p.m. from Horwich Leisure Centre. Entrants will be accepted before the run starts.

Above: Penny's fundraising featured in the local paper.

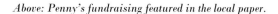

Right: Preparing for a fundraising fun run with Sarah, Carol, Karen, Carol's friend Maria, and Penny.

Right Bottom: Martin and Lorraine Rosekilly and their young son Carl (in headphones) who is now married with a young daughter.

Heaven Sent, Taylor Made

Evidence of more fundraising activities!

Top Left: Andrew Morley and John as clowns. Top Middle: At Bolton's Victorian Market (John, Penny, Judith and Grandma Taylor).
Top Right: Penny dressed up as a tramp with Sarah Whatmough and Sarah Bashall. Other photos are of Penny running, a Victorian
fundraising stall, and a newspaper article about Sarah Whatmough's fundraising.

Penny's passion and energy for fundraising were inspirational to all who knew her.

What friends are for...

SARAH Whatmough of Blackrod set out to do her best for Papworth Hospital Heart and Lung Transplant fund. When she learned that her oldest friend 'Penny' Taylor was on their list to receive the treatment.

Penny is still awaiting a suitable donor, but could be called in any time for the treatment that will give her a new lease on life. Sarah added the £170 cheque to the growing total she has raised in the last few years to help support her best friend's treatment.

Life Goes On

Monsall Hospital became our regular meeting place. As we made our way there ~~would~~ along the stretch of motorway we always wondered 'who we'd see today'. To look at the buildings at Monsall you would not be impressed. They ~~to~~ are spread out ~~and~~ over a large area and their appearance is cold and unwelcoming. A high wall ~~surrounding~~ encloses the wards and the ~~tea~~ stark trees stoop as you pass by. The only birds to visit the grounds are scavengers — crows and magpies — and they add to the forboding presence of brick and slate. As Dr Webb once said, 'it is Du Mauriers birds that ~~perch~~ in those trees.'

Above: Dr Mary Ellis and Penny at Mary's house.

Reverend Denis Gatenby visiting Penny's house. and a cartoon of Denis drawn by Penny that still lives on the Taylor family's fridge!

Dr Webb (fifth from left in black glasses) and the team at Monsall, and (Right) on his own in more recent times (from www.uhsm.nhs.uk).

Dr Dickson retired when Penny was twelve, and she was then given into the care of Dr Mary Ellis at Bolton Royal Infirmary. At this stage, Penny was admitted into hospital with Haemoptysis, a severe bleed, and was on an IV drip for nine days. This definitely put her off needles! On his retirement, Penny wrote to Dr Dickson to keep in touch with him on a personal level and she continued to stay in touch all her life.

Also when Penny was twelve she attended confirmation classes with Lesley at the rectory and both girls were confirmed on May 10th 1983 at St Catherine's Parish Church in Horwich—the two parish churches alternated hosting confirmations. When Penny was fifteen years old, her care was transferred to Monsall Hospital in Manchester under Dr Webb, their Cystic Fibrosis consultant. This was a traumatic time for her as she had felt secure with her care at Bolton. In 1985 Penny was referred to Crumpsall hospital as her periods started and this had caused her further problems. Overall, she had been healthier though and was able to do lots of bike rides and walking with friends, her dad and Freeway.

Above: John's cousin, Joyce, and her husband, Eric, were regular dogsitters for Freeway. Pictured here with their own dog, Sadie.

Penny went to Scotland for a party with her family and this was when she painted 'After the Party' which features at the beginning of this book. She also passed her Grade Four piano exam which made Penny, her family and Mrs Baron very proud. At this time her medication was changed. She'd been taking Pancrex V tablets right from the time of her first diagnosis, but she moved on to a new tablet called Creon which seemed to work much better for her. But, in 1987 Penny noticed that she was becoming more breathless and in the May she once again had a severe Haemoptysis. She was at this time at the sixth form in school and this was just prior to her taking her A levels. However, despite her illness, she was able to complete her A level exams in Art and English.

Unfortunately, she had yet another severe haemorrhage whilst on holiday at her auntie's home in Scotland. These became more frequent and she was admitted to Monsall hospital for two weeks. Consequently, she was unable to attend Art College—a massive blow after all her hard work.

29.10.89.

My dear Penny,

AT LAST I can send you 'Sunshine and Shadows' - a complimentary copy which comes to you with love and very best wishes.

The book is only small but we had to keep the number of pages down because of printing costs.

I am also sending David C and Pete Lloyd a complimentary copy each, plus a few others - one to Princess Alexandra, to the Rev, Roger Royle and special friends.

I hope very much to make a nice bit of money for CF so as I have had 1,000 copies printed, I have my fingers crossed for lots of buyers.

I often think of you and pray you will soon have your transplant.

Writing this at my daughter's home in Thatcham where we are staying as her second babe is due any day so I am like a cat on hot bricks!

A big hug for Freeway.

Love,

Joy (Everett).

SUNSHINE AND SHADOWS

A collection of original poetry
by
Joy Everett

With further contributions from
David Crawford   Penny Taylor
Peter Lloyd   John Alaimo
Glenn Smith

Profits from the sale of this book will be donated to the Cystic Fibrosis Research Trust

Penny and Joy corresponded regularly. Joy had a grandson with Cystic Fibrosis and she was involved in fundraising..

Penny's poem 'My Pesky Cough' appeared in 'Sunshine and Shadows' and we've also included it later in the book.

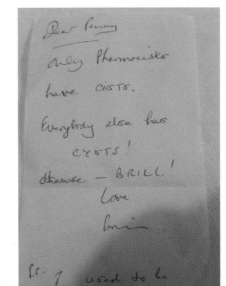

Left: Brian Curson's note about a typo!

Above: The 'Look' newspaper from Autumn 1989.
Two editions were printed and distributed in Horwich, and Penny appeared on the front page of this one.

Life After Formal Education

Above: Judith and John on their surprise anniversary holiday.

The haemorrhages that had stopped Penny from attending Art College became more persistent. If there was no infection accompanying the haemorrhage she could stop it herself by sucking ice, but if there was an infection present then she would have to be admitted to hospital again for IV treatment.

As Penny improved we were able to go on holiday to Tenerife to enjoy some sunshine. Sarah came with us and we all enjoyed the time there with Penny remaining healthy… until the last day! Penny once again started to cough up blood and sucked ice to stop the haemorrhage, but she also became dehydrated. When we got to the airport Penny had to be seen by a doctor before they would consider allowing her to fly. She was given a Vitamin K injection and was left to rest in a private room as the plane was fortunately delayed for five hours. The pilot saw her before agreeing to allow her on the plane and there was plenty of ice on board for her to suck. John had signed a form before we were allowed to board. If we'd had to return to Tenerife because we hadn't got halfway on the journey then we would have had to pay £10,000 in compensation. This came as rather a shock! But we got to Manchester safely and went directly to Monsall where Penny was admitted.

Penny regularly stayed with a family friend called Mary who was in her 80s and both saw this as a wonderful relationship of young and old. Mary was very 'arty' and while staying there Penny planned a weekend holiday for us in Hawkshead – the place where we had spent our honeymoon. She presented this surprise to us in the form of a book based on Freeway, which included lots of sketches, humorous comments and photos, and she even included some 'spending money' for us. All this had been done whilst staying with Mary, so it came as a complete surprise.

Above: Mr Wallwork, the consultant in charge who made the decision about whether Penny could have a transplant.

Above: Two pages from the scrapbook created around Judith and John's holiday to Hawkshead—a treat from Penny.
Below: The holiday hotel.

By January 1988 Penny's condition had deteriorated. She was losing weight, couldn't keep her food down and needed more IV treatment, which we were now able to do at home. She was re-admitted to hospital for three weeks and by June she had lost one and a half stone.

During this time, the vicar of Horwich Parish Church, Rev Dennis Gatenby visited regularly to give Penny Holy Communion and to talk to her about the Bible. When her IV treatment had finished and her Venflons were removed (much to her delight), Penny thanked God for continuing to care for her. Penny was awaiting a transplant. At the age of 19, while awaiting the transplant, Penny was diagnosed with TB and we all assumed that a transplant would not be forthcoming. We saw Dr Webb and he assured us that because they were taking the heart and lungs away, the TB affected areas would also be removed, meaning that she could still get the transplant. Treatment for TB was intravenous, four times a day drips for six months.

Penny with Michele on the beach. Penny was attached to a drip for TB at this time.

Right: Lesley, Penny, Andrew and Freeway in the Taylor family home.

Above: Penny with Michele's baby, Ryan, about a year before her transplant. Michele was the only one of Penny's friends who had a baby that Penny met.

Volunteering for the research study of Cyclosporin Pharmacokinetics.

by, Penny. S. Taylor.

In April this year I took part in a research study. This required extending my regular 3 monthly review and I remained at Papworth from Tuesday until Sunday morning.

A research team from Addenbrookes Hospital were studying the effects of the anti-rejection drug, Cyclosporin, on assessment patients (Cystic Fibrosis or other patients) awaiting heart and lung transplantation.

As a victim of Cystic Fibrosis and having, at that time, awaited transplantation for nine months, I felt that the study might provide interesting and valuable results which could possibly advance the research into treatment for future transplant patients. Therefore, I had no hesitation in agreeing to take part.

I fasted from 10 pm on the wednesday evening, and the study began at 8am the following morning. A small area of my arm was numbed so that a cannula could be fitted, which was later used to take regular blood samples.

The first dosage of cyclosporin was an oral dose. The drug is mixed with orange juice, and though the solution is quite greasy, it is not too unpleasant to swallow. I remained by my bedside for the first four hours following this dose, during which time frequent 1ml blood samples were drawn from the cannula by members of the team. These blood samples were less frequent towards the end of the day.

The following morning a cannula was inserted into my other arm and Cyclosporin was administered intravenously over a 2 hour period. (The dosage in both cases is negligable, and caused no ill effects.) As before, regular blood samples are required and these are drawn from the first cannula.

On the Saturday, blood samples were taken at 8 am and 8 pm, then finally one last sample is required at 8 am on the Sunday morning.

Dear Penny,
You were great on the radio. Congratulations! We have it on tape + it sounds good – will do a copy for you + drop it off.

Thought you'd be tired after all the excitement + I'm in a rush too, so just posting this through. Will be in touch + see you soon. Let us know when you're interviewed again!

Love Jean.

The study was simple and painfree. Admittedly, there is very little activity between blood samples and therefore I was pleased that I had reading materials at hand. The team though are pleasant, understanding, and willing to answer any queries.

But in order to complete their study, more volunteers are required! So far, they have only studied one other Cystic Fibrosis patient.

Research is an ongoing task, but it is vital if advancements are to be made towards more effective treatment, and a better understanding, of transplant surgery. People were volunteering for research when transplants were a new area of surgery. They were the pioneers; but we are the ones who are able to continue to help todays research :- Research such as the study of Cyclosporin pharmacokinetics.

The study is tiring, but without your help advancements in the treatment of transplantation will be a slow process.

The cyclosporin study needs more volunteers, and if you feel you are capable of taking part, then please do.

Maybe the results of this particular study will one day help to save your own life!

Penny travelled to Manchester to be interviewed by Alan Beswick on the 9th of November, 1989. This car from Greater Manchester Radio arrived to pick Penny up from home. Alan was a lovely man who was happy to pose for a photograph with Penny. She was interviewed by him about being on the transplant list, and about the need for more organ donors.

Penny's heart-felt hope ...

On call for transplant

FOR PENNY Taylor, her ultimate ambition is a simple one.

The 19-year-old from Horwich wants to walk up Rivington Pike. But Penny's only hope of doing it is a major operation — a heart and lung transplant.

Penny, of Church Street in Horwich, is waiting for a call from the world-famous Papworth Hospital in Cambridgeshire.

A series of infections has set back her fight against cystic fibrosis, the lung disease she has had from birth, and recently her health has rapidly got worse.

Just four years ago she took part in the Horwich carnival fun run. But last year the former Rivington and Blackrod High School pupil had to give up her hopes of completing a college course after just one week left her exhausted.

Now just getting about the house can be a struggle.

TRANSPLANT DECISION

Penny said of the operation: "There really is no choice as far as I am concerned. I don't want to stay like this. I want to get to the top of the Pike and take a deep breath — something I have never been able to do."

The decision to refer Penny to Papworth was made by the adult cystic fibrosis centre at Monsall Hospital in Manchester, where she receives regular treatment.

Penny's life has been a marathon of hospital visits and treatment at home.

Earlier this month she went with her parents, Judith and John, for a week-long assessment at Papworth before being accepted onto the transplant list.

Said Mr Taylor: "They don't hide anything or attempt to play down the operation. In fact, all three of us were very closely checked for our attitude to the whole thing."

"We were very impressed with the set up — very efficient and caring."

OPERATION RISKS

Papworth has now carried out dozens of transplants, but the operation still has its risks. Although Penny's illness affects her lungs, the heart is transplanted with them because surgeons have found it increases the chance of success.

While at Papworth Penny met another cystic fibrosis sufferer who had been given a heart/lung transplant.

"The transformation is unbelievable," she said. "Now we just have to wait for the call from the hospital."

● Just waiting — that's Penny pictured with pet dog Freeway.

Above: Bolton Evening News 26th July 1988. Right: Penny in 1991, following her transplant. She is looking more healthy again. Her pharmacist friend quipped that Cyclosporin made the legs grow longer!

{ MEMOIRS! }

1) Born 24·6·69 seemingly healthy

2) Diagnosed 13 weeks later — Cystic Fibrosis. [Very little known about it.]

3) Very poorly for 4 mths - nearly died twice.

4) At 7 mths was 11lb heavier than when born. — expected to die at 2 yrs.

5) Lived in a 'tent' till 12 mths old.   Dr Dicksons remedy —
   LOOKED HEALTHY. THOUGH AFTERWARDS!   jelly babies.

6) At 4 yrs - course of injections for bad infection

7) At 4 yrs 3 mths started school :-
   Tablets & physio kept me well

8) At 9 yrs first IV treatment.
   Then went to Dubrovnik   May 1979.

9) 1980 New Zealand.

10) At 11 yrs
    12 yrs } IV. treatment required. B1 ward Townleys.
    15 yrs

11) At 12 yrs haemoptysis started. Went to France. Dr Dickson retired.

12) At 13 yrs was under Dr John Ellis

13) At 15 yrs Mary Ellis was my Dr. and admitted me for I.V. [14 cannulas in 9 days. Completely put me off drips

14) At 15 yrs 3 mths finished my 2wk IV course, still ill, went on nebuliser.
    Transferred to Monsall in October 1984 under Dr Webb. CF clinic.

15) Daunting prospect leaving Townleys !! Stayed well for 2½ yrs.

16) January 1987 - noticed breathlessness.

17) May 1987 - first severe haemoptysis at school prior to A level exams.

18) July 1987 - Second "   "   in Scotland. followed by more frequent
    haemoptysis.

19) Sept 1987 - Very poorly - admitted to hospital for I.V for 2 wks. [Unable to attend Art college!]

    Haemoptysis persisted till December severely.

20) Dec 87 - Went to Tenerife - taken ill, more haem. requiring Vit K injections.
    Dehydrated.
    Admitted to Monsall 15th Dec. Dec. 28" Heart\lung" suggested

21) Jan - Feb 88 - lost weight, poorly, couldn't keep food down.
    More IV treatment for 2 wks at home. (Caeftazidime)

22) March - IV treatment (caeftazidime & tobramycin) - 3 wks hospital.

23) Weight loss by June was 1½ stones. Now 6½ stone from being
    8 stone - december.

24) July 4th - PAPWORTH - July 8th - accepted for heart lung transplant.

25) End July more IV treatment (Caeftazidime)

Penny's own health log.

Night Journey to Papworth— Written by Penny Herself.

NIGHT JOURNEY TO PAPWORTH. *(Original attached)*

Ten minutes into Saturday, 13th May 1989, our phone rang. We'd all been in bed for over an hour though I, for some reason, was finding it difficult to get to sleep. To most people the familiar sound would not have caused much alarm. But for us that insistent ring could only suggest one thing: I was soon to undergo a heart/lung transplant. Instinct informed me that this was the call from Papworth hospital, Cambridge, announcing that a possible donor had at last been found.

In a matter of minutes every nerve-ending in my body was alert.Panic abounded, and I seemed to become suddenly charged with excitement and energy. And though we were all extremely nervous we soon put into action the numerous phonecalls and plans that we had practised so many times before in our minds. This was for real, and within fifteen minutes we had more or less got things organized. A friend from Belmont was on his way over to drive us there; two other friends drove over from Adlington to offer any assistance they could provide; and we collected our suitcases and other luggage which had been sat packed, in a forgotten corner since last July. Our minds raced with tremendous nervous energy,our bodies were instantly ecstatically mobile, and our stomachs felt sick and knotted. Our thoughts questioned the state of the motorway, too, at this late hour on a Friday night - (of all nights') - and we blotted out the nightmarish possibility of traffic jams or other dreaded delays. We had been given three hours to travel the approximate 200 miles and therefore we could not afford to be delayed in any way whatsoever. Our time, from then on, was precious.

Freeway, our dog, was immediately taken, along with his basket and food supplies, to Mrs Lees house, a nearby neighbour who had offered to take care of him. I later realised that I had been unable to say 'Goodbye' to him, but of course that was really the least of my worries.

Whilst the luggage was being loaded into the boot of the car I just had time to make a few phonecalls to some friends. It was 12.30am and I knew that most of them would still be awake, and at 12.35am we set off. Everything had gone to plan so far. Thankfully Mum and Dad had previously been warned by the Transplant Patient Advisor, Virginia O'clock,[*] not to drive as "you won't be in any fit state to do so". She was right too!

The journey had a dreamlike quality. I think we were all in shock, as the dashing scenery outside seemed unreal, and throughout the journey we were totally unaware of time. We passed most of the time cracking jokes. They were corny jokes and for some reason I fail to remember most of them. Some were merely daft comments - "Why've you packed the whiskey in the boot, Dad?" or "Great! I'll get out of that dental appointment next week!" We tried desperately to make light of the situation

* We think this should be 'O'Brien'!

- it seemed the only way we suppress the mounting anxiety. Even the atmosphere in the small casing of the car was intense, and the constantly reminding words - "Tomorrow I'll be able to breathe properly" - boomed in my eardrums. The car catapulted along the dim, endless road into the unknown, unimaginable future. We knew not what to expect at our journeys end and, had I been the driver, perhaps I would have *been* sorely tempted to increase the pressure *on* the brake pedal. But I wasn't the driver. *take the pressure off the accelerator* And the car continued at the same speed for most of the three hour journey.

Cystic Fibrosis, the genetically inherited disease affecting both the lungs and digestive system of the unfortunate victim, was the reason I found myself heading towards Papworth at this late hour. Gradually, over a number of years, numerous infections had attacked my lungs to such an extent that some days just getting round the house proved exhausting. I could walk. And I was still able to go out in the car. But in between 'outings' my life revolved around the chairs in our sitting room. For a nineteen year old girl this sort of daily routine is not much fun! And at times, especially when the weather was providing glorious sunshine, being indoors does tend to get rather frustrating. I find myself wishing I was able to walk Freeway in his much loved park, or simply to walk up the road to post a letter.

And now, suddenly, one phone call had restored new hopes, new ambitions,and ...new fears. On reaching Godmanchester, I felt incredibly sick. It was the typical nausea that appears on the morning of an important exam. But there was no real fear, as such. Merely a tremendous, glowing excitement.

We arrived at the hospital at 3.30am and immediately we made our way towards the Intensive Care Unit. I felt fairly calm, but my stomach told me otherwise. I was met at the door by the Transplant Co-ordinator and as we made our way inside she enquire about the journey. I told her that everything had run smoothly, but I was more concerned as to where the toilets were! A small, round faced nurse hurried up to us requesting a urine sample, though much of what she said passed over our heads. Before long I was taken into a small room and prepared for the operation - blood pressure taken; temperature checked. etc.

I looked on enviously at my three supporters who were sipping hot tea!

Whilst this preparation was in progress the donor organs were being removed which, we were informed, would take an hour. Another patient had also been brought to the hospital in the hope of receiving my heart. This meant that a double transplant was due to take place that night. Understandably I was was now getting quite panic stricken - my life was about to alter immensely. Yet still I felt excited at the prospect. "Well. This is it." I thought, as the transplant co-ordinator returned. It was now 4.40am.

Sadly, her news was quite to the contrary. The donor

organs had been examined and though the heart was perfect, the lungs were infected. The transplant, for me, would not take place that night, but at least the other person was able to receive the donor heart. One of us had benefited.

My feelings at this point were mixed - relief was imminent, but a part of me felt terribly disappointed. Suddenly I wanted to sleep.

The return journey was very quiet. We all felt tired and numb. Numb to the core. And when we stopped at a service station we ate silently and automatically, each of us alone with frustration and fluctuating emotions.

Looking back on Saturday morning I feel happy. At last I am reassured in knowing that I AM being considered seriously for transplantation. Previously I didn't know what to think. The possibility of a heart/lung transplant seemed an impossibility. I know what to expect if I am lucky enough to receive a similar phonecall. We coped this time so I am sure we could cope a second time. Or a third if necessary. And I know that the staff, to whom praise should be acknowledged, will calm and encourage me. I am scared. Undoubtedly. But I strongly believe that transplants of any sort in such circumstances like my own, are essential and extensively beneficial. During the past 18 months many of my Cystic friends at Monsall Hospital in Manchester, have died whilst awaiting heart/lung transplantation, due to the fact that there are simply not enough donors.

Despite recent efforts of both television and newspaper publicity there is still an obvious shortage of signed donor cards. Only signed donor cards consent others to live. These forms are far more advantageous than those which collect dust in doctors waiting rooms or other equally obtainable places.

The present statistic at Papworth for survival is 78% and obviously research into this area can only improve if people, myself included, are willing to undergo surgery. For me there really is no choice - the choice is life or death. It is that simple. But my personal choice is for life. I don't WANT the donor of the organs to die. But if I am granted this unique opportunity to live what others consider to be a 'normal life', then I can only hope that the family of my donor might realise just how much my new life will be appreciated.

No amount of words would ever convey my gratitude.

Of course, there is no written guarantee that there operation will be successful but, with determination, there is no reason as to why it should fail either. Like many other people of my age I have ambitions that I wish to fulfil. My first ambition however, is no different than that of a new born child - an ambition to take the first slow, stumbling steps along the road of life.

When I first mentioned to a certain relative of mine that I had finally, after a six months wait, been accepted onto Papworths heart/lung transplant waiting list (8th July 1988) she simply replied; "Aren't you lucky!"

I believe I am.

'What My Faith Means To Me'

Written by Penny Taylor, August, 1989, while on the transplant waiting list.

It was the last day of December 1987 when my consultant, Dr AK Webb, first tested my faith in him. As a victim of the genetic disease, Cystic Fibrosis, my twenty years have revolved around the regular visits to Bolton and District General Hospital and, from my mid-teenage years, to Monsall Hospital, Manchester.

From an early age I have learned to put my trust in the doctors who have treated me. But when, in a small room in the physiotherapy department, Dr Webb suggested that I underwent a heart and lung transplant, I knew then that this was to be the most challenging test of my faith in him. He was painfully aware that he was making this recommendation to a Fibrocystic patient that he had once regarded as being 'one of the healthiest' in his clinic.

However, during the eight months that had preceded December 1987, I had consistently woken in the morning to discover that a river of blood had lodged in my throat from my lungs. And, though I was loath to admit it, I knew that my health was seriously, steadily deteriorating.

Heart and lung transplants were a new field of surgery at this time and, unaware that transplantation might be a future possibility, I tried to come to terms with the daunting realisation that my life might be short lived. The few days that followed Dr Webb's suggestion were filled with self-pity. 'Why me?' was the question most prominent in my mind. However, my faith in this man never faltered. He was a practical man with practical ideas. But the final decision to be referred to Papworth Hospital, Cambridge, was mine, and was, by no means, an easy choice. (Eighteen year old girls ought to be enjoying life. Not contemplating its meaning!)

But now, one and a half years later, having been accepted onto Papworth's transplant waiting list, I feel assured that I have made the right decision. And though the donors are presently in short supply, the surgeon, Mr John Wallwork, confidently said to me that, if and when a suitable donor was found, he could quite easily 'fit' the donor organs for me, but that it

Michael Holden first saw Penny's name on the prayer list on the church newsletter. It asked for prayers for Penny Taylor at 'Papworth'. He took it to mean that Penny must live at Papworth, and couldn't understand why she was on the Horwich Parish newsletter.

His first introduction to Penny in person was at church, and he was surprised to see her in trousers with spider web patterns on them. They became friends and joined a Bible study group together. At other times they went out together. Michael would borrow his father's car and would take Penny off to the cinema in places like St Helens, where Penny had never been before. They remained friends till Penny died.

After her death, Michael realised how upset we were at not only losing Penny, but by the fact that we would never be grandparents, and even though he wasn't married at that time, he told us that one day he would make us grandparents—and, true to his word, he did.

He is now married to Jennifer and has two children, Georgia and Noah. We still see Michael and his family occasionally.

was 'up to me to get them going!' With this in mind I put my trust in him, and returned home to await the call.

The second area of my faith lies in myself. Without this, I would be without ambition. It must be remembered though that some aspects of life require help and support from others. I depend upon certain people to guide and advise me. My parents have always been honest about my illness, explaining things to me from an early age, and this has helped me to accept my situation. But self confidence plays an important part, and without it I would be unable to make my own decisions.

Because I believe in myself I am able to make judgements of my own, and realise and appreciate my capabilities. Although my own judgement has not always proved to be accurate, I am always willing to learn from my mistakes.

The most vital channel of my faith is in God. I will not attempt to even try to explain who, or what, God is. But what I will admit is that I gain a great deal of my strength from my belief in Him. I have been a member of the congregation of the Holy Trinity Church for many years and, although I sat through many of the Sunday School lessons giggling with my friend, Lesley, I always felt that I 'belonged' at Church. I offload my worries and fears onto God, and in return he gives me the support I need to live each day. He provides me with a positive attitude, and I am reassured in knowing that He will help me through these long months of uncertainty.

1987
1984   **January**

SERIOUSNESS.

Sunday   **22**
22–344   Week 3
3rd after Epiphany

Why DO people take life so very seriously? They seem to live each day unaware of their actual being, only concious of what they own and of what they want. Selfish. Yes, I would say so yet who am I to say? Do I not also indulge in self needs, self pity and selfishness from time to time? Of Course! But how many people, I wonder, are actually aware they are living such unruly lives?

Indeed, we DO live in a tragic age, oblivious to matters of the heart and unaware of the fact that we live each day without questioning it's meaning; it's uncanny reason.

Some might say "I'll never die" and continue to live the life of a laquered yahoo whilst others may view life as a stage, where we make a grand entrance, read our lines then make our exit, leaving pitiful onlookers to question "What must it be like?".

Some may fight, determined to conquer death or override that great abyss which divides the earth and the heavens. Diseased and crippled they go on, determination gripping their inward soul; a determination which brings strength and courage. Is it possible, we ask, to be serious of such a complex game?

That great city Babylon; that famous prostitute, cries out in desperation; doom inevitable. The over indulgence of those elements which keep the nations on a permanent "high" causes their own destruction. They sIN. Sin such as was never seen before. Intoxicated on their own lustful odour; persuits; oblivious to their seriousness.

Indeed, they ARE serious. They grasp their persuits and hold them high on a pedistal of gold. This pedistal is their life force; a tower on which sits sIN, proud and gleaming.

But when their pedistal collapses around them and falls, crashing, to their feet, and death approaches with an almighty smile, who will they blame? What will be left to say?

In God ONLY there is life! Yes, when realization sinks in .... That's what they'll say.

By. Penny. T.

Transplant(s) at Last

Above: Judith, Keith Seddon, Penny and Andrew Keely. Keith and Andrew were of great assistance helping with transport around the time of Penny's transplant. The Seddons were terrific neighbours and looked after our home while we were away. They even paid bills.

Left Top: Keith with his son, Christopher.

Left Bottom: Keith's wife, Wendy and Chris, with dog Loui.

We were lucky enough to stay at the house of our friends, Jean and Andrew Keeley while they were away with their children, Paul and Joanne.

John, Penny, Andrew and I had a lovely time exploring around the area nearby. Andrew took his dinghy and went on the 'Blue Lagoon'. Back at the house we would play snooker, cards and other games. Penny also wrote many poems, including 'Holiday in Belmont' reproduced later in the book. We were only a few miles from home but it was very quiet and relaxing.

When Penny was ill, she lost a lot of weight. Jean made some padding and sewed it into her trousers so that it was more comfortable when she sat down.

In the months before her transplant, Penny's quality of life had deteriorated, and she was limited in the activities she could do. By that time, she was struggling to walk and weighed very little. Her friend, Andrew Morley, took her to Manchester and would carry her round on his back. He also took her up Rivington Pike on his back and was always there to help her.

John and I took Penny to Monsall to see Dr Webb and he informed us that Penny now had only ½ litre of air in her lungs and that she could not sustain herself at this level for very long. On the way home after seeing Dr Webb we called at the vicarage to see Rev John McGrath. Penny and I stayed in the car because it was raining very heavily and John went into the vicarage on his own. Rev John McGrath came out to the car to see Penny and we opened the window so that they could chat. He had brought some holy oil out with him and anointed Penny with the sign of the cross on her forehead and then just said, 'Tonight' with no explanation. We went home and had our tea and then at 7:45 pm, Papworth rang to say that they had a donor. So, it really was 'Tonight'. We rang our friend, Andrew Keely, who lived nearby in Belmont and asked him to take us down as it was recommended that we should not drive ourselves. Our next door neighbor, Keith Seddon, then followed in our car so that we would have transport when we were there, and Andrew then brought Keith back home. Penny was prepared for her transplant and we were taken into the nurses' quarters and given a bedroom for the night. As we walked across the courtyard to the building, John and I suddenly experienced a feeling of calm and peace as though God was taking care of us. We actually managed to sleep, as we remained calm and secure in

Rev John McGrath. Before Penny got the transplant he anointed her as they called at his house on the way back from Monsall.

Above: Jean and Andrew Keeley who helped Penny and we used to stay in their house when they were away.

Medical Miracles article on page 46 of Take a Break 14 April 1990

About Andrew Jackson

'*For most of his early years, Andrew Jackson could only sit and watch the other kids playing football. Andrew was born with a heart riddled with defects... But they never gave in—and neither did Andrew.*

The courage finally paid off last November when surgeons at Newcastle's Freeman Hospital carried out one of the most complex heart transplants ever, transforming the 'blue' and breathless football fan into a healthy pink schoolboy.

Before the Op

'*Every minute of every day, Susan and Ken knew exactly where to find each other. The ambulance crews and airline staff were on constant stand-by for the day when a heart became available. Andrew, in the meantime, needed more and more treatment to keep him alive...*

'*We'd always known a transplant would be his only hope but, because of the defects, he could have a heart only from someone with similar defects. A transplant from a living donor was his best chance, but the odds were pretty remote.*'

But last November a 19-year-old Lancashire girl, suffering from cystic fibrosis, was given a new heart and lungs... and in turn her heart was rushed to Newcastle for Andrew... (who got a) new lease of life three days before his 11th birthday...

Just three days after being wheeled into the operative theatre—cheekily asking the surgeons: 'Now do you know what you are doing, have you done this before?'—Andrew was sitting out of his bed and celebrating his birthday... Two weeks later he was home...

Andrew's parents:

'*For Susan and Ken, trying to put into words what they feel for Dr Baines, Mr Darke and his team, and the girl whose heart now beats inside their lovely son, is near impossible. 'She's called Penny. I wrote to her straight away and sent her a picture of Andrew through the transplant co-ordinator. He'd love to meet her—that would be something really special for us.*''

God's love, and better able to face what lay ahead. The operation lasted four hours and went well.

Penny herself became an organ donor as part of the process. This 'domino' transplant occurred because her own heart, which was perfect, could be transplanted independently. It was felt that a simultaneous transplant of heart and lungs was the most successful option for a transplant in a CF patient. Penny's heart was transported in an ice-box up to Newcastle's Freeman Hospital.

Not long after her transplant, Penny was reading an article in 'Take a Break' magazine about a boy from Newcastle—another Andrew! He'd had a heart transplant and she felt sure that it was her heart he'd received. We later found out that this was true, and we asked at Papworth if we could have their contact details as Penny was a living donor. We became friends with the whole family, and they came to visit us, and Penny and Andrew appeared together on Lorraine Kelly's television programme.

Andrew is now forty one years old. He received Penny's heart thirty years ago, and he has experienced no rejection problems whatsoever. His parents are still in contact with John and I and they joke that Penny Taylor's heart was 'tailor made' for Andrew! That's the title of this book.

Penny stayed in hospital for two months with ongoing monitoring daily. She started an exercise routine to help her recovery, including using an exercise bike. We would take her out for the day to visit nearby sites such as Cambridge to get her used to everyday life again. We all stayed in a flat at Papworth which was to ensure that Penny could return to 'normal' life. On one occasion she had to be re-admitted to hospital as she had developed a drug-induced form of diabetes and needed to be stabilised again. After another short stay in the flat we were able to return home, much to everyone's delight.

Penny had to complete a daily diary of her medication and health – and this was a rather scary time after the 'cocoon' of being cared for by staff at Papworth. She still went to Monsall to see Dr Webb and our GP, Dr Panja, called regularly to the house. Other than that, she was living a fairly normal life—seeing her friends, going out, and returning to college to continue her art course, which unfortunately she became unable to continue as she was so ill.

Her vocal cords had been damaged during the transplant operation and she was unable to speak except in a whisper.

Eventually she had an operation at Manchester North Hospital where Teflon was applied to the damaged cords to enable her to speak more easily. She spent her days at home writing poetry and doing artwork as well as continuing to see her friends and going out cycling. In 1990 she travelled to Glasgow to compete in the Transplant Games, for which she received a commemorative medal.

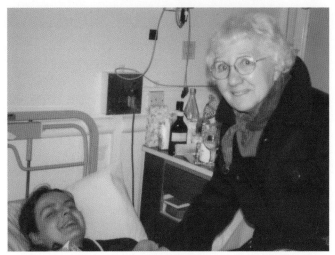

Penny and her grandma, Vera (John's mum) at Papworth after the transplant.

By 1991 Penny was enjoying good health and filling her days with lots of activities. As a family we went with her boyfriend, Andrew Morley, on a cycling holiday to Derbyshire.

Penny was aware that if any complications developed from her transplant while we were away then both Papworth and Monsall were within easy travelling distance and this gave her security. This was a most memorable holiday and we achieved days out that we would never have thought possible.

We stayed in a rented bungalow and Penny spent lots of time researching where we could visit on both wet and dry days. We visited the Blue John Mines, and the Well Dressing in Tissington by following the High Peak and Tissington trails. We also spent time in Ashbourne.

One day we were out and as it was going dark the heavens opened, so we gingerly made our way down to the main road and into the local pub for a meal and to get warm. But then we had to go back on the trail to get back to the car. Not easy!

A smiling Doctor Panja. She was a good doctor and was very involved in Penny's life and illness from 1988 onwards.

Penny loved cycling and we would often put our bikes on the back of the car and go to Fleetwood. We would then cycle along the prom towards Blackpool. We also went into Derbyshire for days out and again cycled along the trails.

One of our favourite places to stay was the Lake District cottage belonging to our friends. They allowed us to stay there often and it was always a delight. Penny and our friend shared a sense of humour and he would leave a message in their grandchild's cot indicating that it was for Penny. Penny in turn would leave a baby's bottle, complete with teat, in the cot when we left

Above: John and Judith at Papworth.

Some people ask me what it's like
To live with 'someone else inside'.
They ask me what it's like to feel
A brand new heart and lungs beside.
At first, I'd say, it's like false teeth –
They seem to feel so 'tight' and new.
They also creak and squeak a lot
    Reminding me of a new shoe.
I asked a friend how long it takes
To feel that they have settled in;
He said to leave it for three months –
'You'll notice a difference then!'
I know it took me quite a while
To adjust to once again being well –
And with all the drugs I had to take
At first, well I just couldn't tell!
It was 'swallow this' and 'inject that'
    And 'mind you have your drip'.
    And 'don't' forget to nebulise'
    And 'drink your Fortisip'.
The list went on and on and on –
    An endless pill-pop session.
    It seemed to me to simply be
    An educating lesson.
    But now, a year is over with.
    They feel quite content with me
    And I know I feel so proud to say
    That I'm a transplantee.

saying 'This is for baby in his cot'. On our last holiday together, we spent time in the Lakes and by this time Penny was on daily oxygen. But Penny would never give up and in fact her last bike ride was up The Street in Rivington village with the oxygen tank strapped to her bike.

In September 1991 Penny was admitted to Papworth hospital again, and part of her transplanted lung was removed. Rev Paul Duffett and his wife Anita accommodated John, Penny's boyfriend Andrew and myself in their home for three weeks at this time. This was a very kind gesture and we remained friends afterwards.

Above: Denis Gatenby and his wife Dorothy. Dorothy kindly selected the betrothal verse for Penny and Andrew's engagement.

The Church and all Penny's friends were very supportive. Both Rev Dennis Gatenby and Rev Jonathon Carmyllie came often to pray and chat with Penny. She was now unable to eat and relied on oxygen daily.

Penny's boyfriend, Andrew, had asked Rev Gatenby to perform a marriage ceremony, but unfortunately, this was not legal as Penny was on morphine. It was therefore agreed that Rev Gatenby would oversee and bless their engagement using an old betrothal service which the vicar's wife, Dorothy, had been able to find. They exchanged engagement rings.

Penny was aware that this time she would not survive her declining health so designed her own funeral service and service sheet, including requesting that everyone should wear bright colours for the ceremony. She slept with me every night to ensure that she was comfortable throughout the night.

One night at midnight, Penny woke me up and asked for a sheet of paper and a pen. It was then that she wrote 'Sleepers Shore' which features a little later in the book.

Have you not quacked on yet..
I love you, ducky.

you know, your finer points attract me.

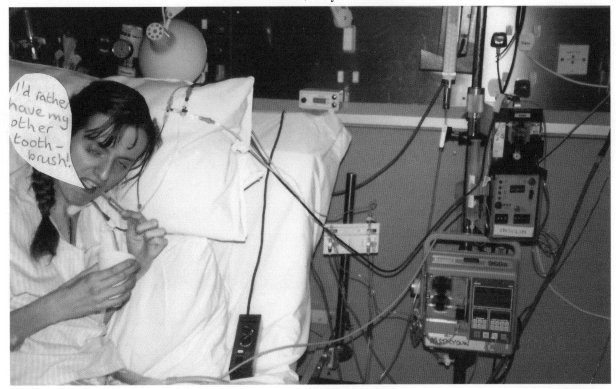

Even during Penny's most difficult moments, her sense of humour shone through.

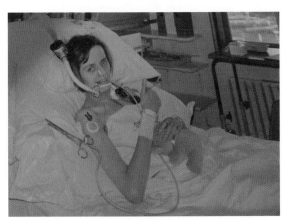

Above: Penny in hospital looking so frail but hopeful.

Penny and Freeway after she began taking Cyclosporin. This photo was used on her door in Papworth.

Paul and Joanne Keeley (children of Andrew and Jean) with the ducks at Papworth. Penny's room can be seen in the background.

Penny and the surgeon, Stephen Large, who performed her transplant.

Penny's Auntie Margaret wrote a poem about a Christmas tree that waited for Penny to come home from hospital.

The Tree that waited
21/1/90.

I'm the tree that waited but my duty's now done,
To the last of the family, I've just given some fun,
Trying to guess which of my finery is new,
Emma, David and Charlotte tried and now Penny too,
But every year of pink and silver there is more,
Dragging my branches down near to the floor,
I'd hid all the chocolate but now they are all gone,
Taken by all the children, one by one,
So now gradually I am being unwound,
Of the tinsel that has wrapped me round,
The shiny balls and animals and things,
Are placed in their boxes alongside the angel with wings
The crackers that I was so delighted to see,
Are slid from my branches and taken away from me,
And last of all, my fairy on top,
But still none of my needles did I drop,
For I am a Scotch pine and very proud of it,
Even though on me no more lights will be lit,
So tonight I stand all forlorn,
Of all my glitter I have been shorn,
No hope for me as I'm taken outside,
What use now my silly pride?

As the night drew on a large light shone,
On my branches which frost rested on,
And I started to glimmer and gleam,
A new life for me, is this a dream,
In the morning I was delighted to see,
Some fresh new presents being hung on me,
Bird cake, coconut and nuts in gold mesh,
And containers with breadcrumbs nice and fresh,
For now I see I have a new job to do,
Keeping the birds fed all winter through,
And as they hop and peep about,
It takes me all my time not to shout out,
The nuts are here, the bread there,
But if I did it would only scare,
So I let my new friends search around,
And find a refuge safe off the ground,
I'll do my new job and keep my pride,
Robin, Bluetit and Sparrow safe inside,
As another night comes I keep them warm and dry,
Underneath the dark and glittery sky,
Once more my branches come alive with light,
Oh yes, I am beautiful and what a sight,
I'm the tree that waited for my best job yet,
Even though it is cold and I may get wet!!
LOVE AUNTIE H.

Above: Penny with childhood friend, John Duckworth, and John's parents Kath and Les, after the transplant.

Top Right: Linda and David at the back, then Auntie Ruth, Michael, Uncle George and Sarah. Penny was Sarah's godmother. Ruth and George looked after Penny a lot and Penny loved to visit Uncle George in his garden to help out.

Underneath This: Penny, Auntie Margaret and Uncle Eric, in front of the tree that waited.

Above: David, Emma, Deborah and Penny in front of the tree that waited.

Left: Our last Christmas (1991) with Auntie Dorothy, Andrew, Penny and Grandma Taylor, with performing dog, Freeway.

Tales from the dollhouse.

Hello dear Penny, Auntie Margaret's verse time here,
I bet you've been wondering when it would appear,
I've thought of you often, especially at night,
Waking and wondering if you are all right,
And then the poetry has come into my head,
But not writing it down it will remain unread,
So I am jotting these few lines after 'Top of the Pops',
The house is quiet now, Eric's gone to the shops.
I've lots to tell you so I hope you've got time,
Between the routine of seeing doctors hopefully benign

On Tuesday the 1st to London I go,
To look at the dresses hung in a row,
At Harrods, Selfridges, John Lewis and the very best,
The shops on South Molton Street stand out from the rest.
I'm going with Alison who is on a diet,
So we are going to be living on salad,
But do not worry that I'll fade away,
Because at 'Garfunkels' salads rule the day.

3/
I'll get those in London where I'm sure to find
Just the pair I can't possibly leave behind,
So you just hurry to get well,
Come home soon with tales to tell,
We'll get together and I'll tell you mine,
And we'll all have a lovely time.

Lots of Love from Auntie Margaret.
26th September 1991.

P.S. Do you think these poems are
getting cornier and cornier !!!.

A poem written to Penny from her Auntie Margaret.

2/
For £4.50 you just help yourself
And what a selection on the shelf,
In the evening on Italien we usually dine
Alison can have melon but the lasagne is mine,
We come back late on Thursday and then
I'll have to rush,
Just over a week will be a bit of a push,
To make Deborah's 21st party dress and
finish her cake,
You know what I'm like and how long it
will take.
She doesn't want the cake fancy but in my
hands,
The icing tube can't stop making fancy curves
and bands,
I've made the roses, thats one job less,
But Noddy and Big Ears with their clothes
are not blessed,
I've finished my dress though, a concoction
in pink,
I just need some new earrings the colour to link

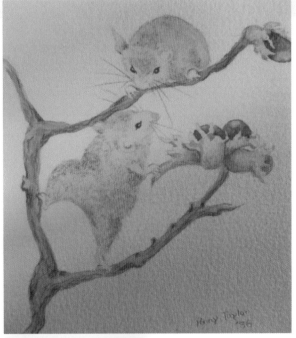

Penny's gorgeous watercolour of climbing rodents, plus a few other cute examples of her artistry!

Penny's 21st Party

Above: Chris and Brian Curzon held Penny's 21st party at their house after Penny's transplant. Brian had even taken Penny to Papworth, and regularly helped out the family.

Above: Andrew's mum, Penny, Margaret and Andrew at the party.

Above: Sharon, Michele and Sarah Bashawe at the party.

Below: John Duckworth, Judith and Margaret.

Alison, Sarah and Penny, with Mark who was a friend of John Duckworth.

Whose Heart? by Penny Taylor, 11th June 1980

Written from the point of view of Penny's heart.

We were writing to the media this time. 'For support' she had said, hoping that they might help us to raise some public interest in the relatively new area of surgery; transplantation. Penny was a believer in transplantation and hoped, one day, to undergo a heart and lung transplant herself, having spoken to and seen others who had benefited from it themselves. I agreed that transplantation, from what I had seen, was a marvelous thing, but I was not too sure as to whether I fully believed in it myself.

It was June 1989 and her friends at Monsall Hospital, in Manchester—friends, whom at that time, she had grown to know and love over a 12 month period—were, one by one, dying. It seemed to be an unending sadness. The doctors and medical staff were at a loss to know what to do for the best; treatment no longer seemed to be effective for some of her friends; and foremost in all our minds we could not help but wonder 'who would be next..?'

And so, it was for this reason, and out of sheer desperation, that we now turned to national media for their support. The reason for the unnecessary number of deaths amongst her friends was due to the vast shortage of donors. They didn't WANT people to die. They simply hoped that, should tragedy occur in a family, they would consider donating for transplantation. But, in order for this wish to be carried out, we wanted to stress the importance of discussing their wishes to donate for transplant surgery, now. Not in six months time when, by then, it may already be too late to discuss it.

Penny's wish was to publicise the importance of discussion amongst families on this subject, but, as she sat writing numerous letters to various places, my own wishes differed to hers. I was reluctant to support her at this stage.

Penny and I had grown up together. And I, being her heart and always beating strong and healthy inside her, had grown very fond of her. I had no wish to be removed! We had both experienced many good times, along with times of personal grief, over our twenty years together and, to my mind, we were a good team. I did not wish to exchange a 'good home' for the confines of a specimen jar or, even worse, an incinerator in a hospital. I was happy to stay where I felt I belonged.

It was Penny's lungs that were the problem – they were the ones that were damaged. They had bled a lot during the last two years causing her a great deal of stress and worry, and causing me to palpitate due to worry and lack of oxygen. Those lungs were nothing but a nuisance to us both. Penny shared the same illness as her friends; the genetic disease, Cystic Fibrosis. It didn't affect me but over the years, due to constant bouts of infection, it had damaged her lungs beyond repair. Many of her friends were seriously ill and, like Penny, their only chance of survival was to undergo heart and lung transplantation. Penny had already explained that if she was lucky enough to be a recipient of transplantation I had no choice but to be replaced in order to increase her chances of survival. This is where I disapproved! But at the same time I didn't want her to die due to my own selfishness. So we tried to find ways of compromising and it was, in fact, her hospital in Cambridge—Papworth Hospital—that had come up with ideas that would help us to agree to terms.

They discussed a thing called 'domino'—though I was at a loss to know why a game should have anything to do with this matter—but I immediately made it quite clear to them that I was happy to go along with this 'game' providing that they did not pickle or incinerate me. I had no intentions of spending the rest of my days viewing the world from a glass jar. I was no goldfish!

They laughed. 'Don't worry,' they said, 'we have better plans for you!' I was unsure as to what they meant, but Penny seemed happy enough with these 'plans'—I would just have to trust that she knew what she was doing with our futures.

For her friends, all of whom were in their early twenties, transplantation was required urgently. And, feeling so helpless and not knowing what else to do, it was decided that first we would appeal to the popular television programme 'That's Life' for their help. We asked them to emphasise the shortage of donors, and to highlight how so many people have, in the past, benefitted from transplantation.

To our joy, they responded!

They enquired if any of the Fibrocystic patients were able to travel to their London studio, to appear on that week's programme. All were too ill though so it was suggested that Paul, brother to her friend Sarah, appear on the show on behalf of Sarah and her friends. Sarah's need was perhaps the greatest because she was so ill. He was nervous but he managed to speak clearly of how his sister, Sarah—a dear friend whom Penny had first met two years previously—was desperately ill in hospital and required an operation of this sort, soon. Three Fibrocystic patients who had already undergone the surgery appeared on the show and were bursting with enthusiasm for transplantation. Each spoke of the tremendous difference it had made to their lives, and they looked so healthy.

It saddened me when the plight of a young boy of ten years of age was mentioned on the programme. The fair-haired youngster required a heart transplant and I realised then how lucky Penny and I were to have survived twice the number of his years. The boy's lips were a sinister shade of deep plum and he had to be carried everywhere as he suffered from five major heart defects. It was obvious to me, being a healthy heart, that inside this boy a very poorly heart indeed was struggling to keep him alive.

The programme ended, the message had been said, and Penny finally felt that maybe we were beginning to get somewhere. Now we needed to follow up the publicity in other ways, and using different methods. Perhaps, we considered, the national newspapers might be willing to help us. We began following up our ideas. But our tears of joy were soon to return to sadness. Three days later, with her immediate family around her bedside, Sarah died. It was the 28th June, she was 20 years old and should, like any other girl of that age, have been about to embark on the best years of her life. Her death destroyed our hopes and, devastated, our enthusiasm was crushed.

Penny withdrew into her grief. And I withdrew, taking refuge between her lungs which had swollen now to such an extent that when Penny went for a heart scan they would no longer find me. 'Well.' They told her, 'you've definitely got a heart in there somewhere!' Yes, I was here, but I refused to show myself. I was small enough to stay hidden and there, warm and secure between the two gross, damaged lungs, I remained.

By November, Penny was the only surviving person at her clinic on an active transplant waiting list. Three more of her friends had died, although they too had been on active lists for a number of months beforehand. The overwhelming sadness, and even greater sense of loss, sparked a small flame of enthusiasm within her and, having the heart of a poet, she wrote, during a moment of utter despair, a poem which she later decided to make use of by sending it to every major national newspaper she could think of. Her friends supported her and helped her to dispatch the poem, which described the sadness of losing loved ones and of the waste and senselessness of allowing two people to die when there need only be one 'Goodbye'. Once the poem, and the enclosed forwarding letter, had been posted, we could do nothing, only wait for replies. And hope…

However, we had no luck!

This left us feeling despondent for we were aware that alone it was impossible to raise public awareness on a national scale. Our only aim was to prove that transplantation WAS beneficial and deserved future research into this area of modern surgery. But without both knowledge and proof that this was indeed a worthwhile operation, the public were unlikely to respond.

It seemed as though we were getting nowhere fast and I recalled the words of a relative of Penny when we told her that she had been accepted onto Papworth Hospital's transplant waiting list in July 1988. 'Aren't you lucky!' she had exclaimed. But Penny, not eighteen months on, was beginning to question whether she was actually on that list, or not.

We were no nearer now than we had been then, and during the period of January to November of 1989, Penny had already lost ten of her friends, because there were no donor organs available. She did not consider herself to be lucky having lost one friend for each month that had passed that year.

Two weeks later a miracle happened.

Her transplant took place!

When we received the call, I became alarmed—nay, panic-stricken—and begged her not to go through with it. But she wouldn't listen. We had been given just 3 hours to rush to Papworth Hospital, 200 miles away! Penny was ecstatic though, and chattered happily throughout the journey. I, on the other hand, thought dismally about specimen jars and worst of all, incinerator. Was that really to be my own destiny, along with those awful lungs which, by now, were taking up more room than ever? I was really quite crushed between them these days.

It was the night of November 16th and we arrived at the surgical ward at 11:30pm.

It had taken just three hours to make the journey.

Above right: Andrew Jackson with Kevin Keegan before the transplant. All dressed up in his Newcastle strip!

Somewhere in the land, a family were going through immense personal loss at that time and yet, as we rushed towards the intensive care area, I wondered if they knew how much joy and hope they had given—so generously—to Penny and her family. They had given them a future once more and, if all went well, a healthy future too. That would be something Penny had never fully experienced before. In some ways I did feel happy for her and I beat rapidly inside her to let her know this, but secretly I felt sad that soon we were to be parted. In truth, I did not want to move out.

At 3:00am on the 17th of November, Penny was ready for surgery and word came through that the donor heart and lungs—much to my own disappointment—were perfect. A perfect match! The last thing that Penny remembered was a kind face peering over her; a reassuring hand clutching hers; and a gas mask over her face, supposedly to relieve the pain caused by the insertion of a neck line. As the pain subsided, I began to calm myself, beating now at an almost normal rate despite my apprehension, whilst Penny, opening her eyes briefly before going into a deep sleep, said 'I feel alright now…'

Suddenly I heard a voice in the outside corridor. 'I've come to pick up an unattached heart' boomed the voice. 'Sorry mate, but you'll have to wait,' replied another voice, 'it's still inside my daughter'.

Someone was talking about me! Obviously (though at the time I could not understand why) I was about to be chauffeured to my destination by a Securicor man. I was still convinced that I would end up in a bottle at this stage. I cried a few blood red tears as I left Penny, though she looked peaceful as I said 'Goodbye'. The journey that followed was quick, though tiresome; I had never been as cold in my life before! I was stuffed into a dark, freezing cold box, and sent by road and air to another hospital at Newcastle. Before I realised it, my surroundings were very similar to those in which I had left Penny, but here a young boy was being operated on. He was very blue, and I watched whilst a group of people removed his heart and, briefly catching a glimpse of it, it looked of no use to anyone. This heart really was fit for nothing other than a specimen jar!

It was then that the strangest thing happened.

A large, gloved hand picked me up and placed me inside the boy's chest. At first, I was unable to understand what they were planning to do and then—what joy!—it suddenly dawned on me that this was to be my new home! Very carefully the surgeon began to stitch me inside this little boy which, although it was a tight squeeze, was eventually comfortable. Much better than a specimen jar!

At first, as I got to know this boy, I wasn't too sure as to whether or not I really got on with him. I had

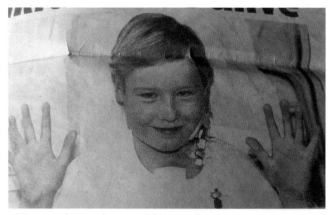

Above: Andrew at the time of the transplants.

Above : Penny with Andrew Jackson about six months after their transplants.

Above: An early Christmas list that Andrew sent to Penny.

never lived inside a boy before and I soon discovered that they have different likes and dislikes to those of a girl. Within two weeks though I was settled—and I felt happy. So, he took me home with him.

Young Andrew Jackson and his family.

We actually get on great now. He has never rejected me, and he treats me to new games such as football, but much to my delight he takes me cycling. Cycling is my favourite hobby!

Andrew and I are doing fine. I wasn't too keen when he started school again in January—I had already been through the stress of exams once and I didn't relish the thought of retakes! I knew now that Penny must have planned this all along, hoping that when the time came someone might be able to give me a new home. I should have known she would never let me down. Now I realised why she had always been in favour of transplantation. I just hoped that her new organs were as happy and content as I was. It pleased me to see Andrew's pleasure and I knew I was doing

Above: Andrew Jackson's brother Christopher, Andrew Jackson, his mum Susan, his dad Ken and his twin sister Sarah.

great; after all, I was of no further use to Penny. Transplantation relies on this—when a healthy organ is of no further use to a person, whether they are alive or dead, a transplanted organ can save another life.

How much more courage it must have taken the family of Penny's donor to make that decision, though. They had been forced to make that choice without warning, whereas Penny had obviously had a lot of time to consider where I was going. She had never doubted that she would survive the operation so she had carefully made plans that I might be provided with new accommodation.

Andrew is gaining his independence once more, and with it his confidence is growing. Transplantation does take a lot of readjustment. 'No-one ever said it would be easy,' I well remember Penny's parents warning her once. Admittedly, it is tough, both physically and psychologically. But with each day I grow stronger inside Andrew and it's great when he wakes each morning, feeling healthy. As the dawn light floods his room and we awake with a new-found energy, this gives the determination to keep on fighting for a bright future.

Thanks to the skill of those dedicated surgeons who performed this amazing domino transplant, and to all those who prepared Penny beforehand and organized the transport to take me 300 miles to another hospital to save this youngster's life, I am reminded why, at this time last year, Penny turned to the media. It was to let the public know that transplantation is fantastic surgery. Is it only a year since we asked for their support?

And to anyone who is still doubtful about transplant surgery, let me tell you that last week I was lucky enough to meet up with Penny. I have never seen her looking so healthy. I could never provide her with those pink nails and lovely pink lips that she now has. It was so good to see her looking so energetic. She was telling Andrew, who took me back home to where I had lived for 20 years with Penny, how much walking she is capable of doing once more. And she hopes to return to art college this September. It was nice being in those old, familiar surroundings for a little while. I looked around and saw the piano, still standing against the far wall where it has always been. How many times, I reminisced, had those

favourite pieces of music stirred and pleased me whilst Penny was playing them? How often had I danced to their bright melodies?

And I recalled other times too when Penny had confided to a close friend that the latest 'wretched boyfriend' had broken me. I tried, at those times, to reassure her that it would take more than that to break me. Did she not realise how strong I had always been? Could she not feel how strongly I beat inside her?

Andrew is now a bright, happy boy of 11 years of age—no different to any other boy of his age. He is an avid football fan and he spends hours on that new mountain bike of his. In fact, in October this year, he is taking me to America to visit Disneyworld in Florida. It will be my second visit to America, for 10 years ago—when he was no more of a year of age—I went to Los Angeles' Disneyland with Penny.

Ask Andrew yourself, and he will point out that he is now 'pink all over! Just like you!' But ironically, he was once that plum-lipped poorly little boy who was suffering from five major heart defects and, like so many other people today in need of transplant surgery, he was dying…

It was for this reason—to achieve public awareness—that we had turned to the media. Ask me, and I will say that a certain relative of Penny's replied wisely when we told her, two years ago, that we had been accepted onto Papworth's transplant active list:

For we really are very lucky indeed!

THE ZIPPER CLUB
BRITISH CARDIAC PATIENTS ASSOCIATION

"For the Benefit of Cardiac Patients & Families throughout the British Isles."

April 1992

Andrew Jackson with his family and his fiancée Gemma. This heart is clearly doing very well.

Lorraine Kelly

Penny and Andrew Jackson appeared on the Lorraine Kelly show talking about their domino transplant. Lorraine was a gracious host and replied to the author personally when permission was requested to use this photo in the book. Since his transplant, Andrew has thrived!

Dear Lorraine,

Thirty years ago this year on 17th November, our daughter Penny Taylor had a heart and lung transplant operation at Papworth hospital Cambridge. On the same night there was another transplant taking place at the Freeman Hospital, High Heaton, Newcastle-Upon-Tyne, Tyne and Wear, NE2 2DN.

The recipient at Freeman hospital, his name is Andrew Jackson, who was ten years of age at the time, and he was given Penny's heart. They were able to meet and he came to Horwich with his parents and it was great to see them both together. They had an interview with you on television from Manchester.

Sadly, Penny died at the age of 22½ years, but Andrew is still living and we keep in touch with his family at Christmas.

I am hoping to publish a book this year on Cystic Fifrosis, and being a transplant recipient. Penny suffered from cystic Fibrosis, which was why she needed a heart and lung transplant.

I would like to use a photograph which was taken off the television at the time of your interview with them. I would like to mention your interview in my book, but I also realise that I need your permission to do so, which is what this letter is about.

Andrew and his family are happy with me using what material I have got.

Yours sincerely,

Judith May Taylor (Mother of the late Penny Taylor)

itv

Dear Judith

Of course you can use the photograph.
I'd be honoured.
I remember the story so well and I'm very sorry Penny died so young.
Good luck with the book.
I'd love to read it.

Lorraine x

Lots of love x
Lorraine

THIS IS'NT REALLY MY BODY

I JUST BORROWED IT!

1 Wk 2 DAYS OVER T/PLANT.

MONDAY. AT PAPWORTH.
27H November 1989.

Dear Mum & Dad.

Hi! Things are pretty good here - well, as good as can be expected! It's not ½ as good without you two but me and my furry friends are coping- I feel GREAT. My blows are averaging 140-150 overall, which they're pleased with. I have - wait for it - no major rejection problems and therefore need no F·O·B's yet. But I do have that common transplant infection so I'm on 10-14 days I.V. I'm now off Caeftazidime, but I'm on insulin on and off depending upon my reaction to the drugs. My exercising is good - now experiencing a lovely healthy ache in the legs which makes me want to get GOING. My only really problem is high doses of Cyclosporin! DRATS! However, they say that's something I'll either have to accept or hope that they can do something about it as time goes by. I really am miffed though about that. STILL. I can't complain.

I had a surprise visit today - Mr. Wallwork, Mr. Large & all THE GANG descended on me. Poor Mr. W. got told in two minutes flat everything I felt good about, he was exhausted just listening to me! I said I felt like a queen and they all burst oot laughing - then I realized why: Queens don't have it SO good do they! He was thrilled I am doing so well, he couldn't believe it, but then he told me the REALLY BAD NEWS: "Penny" he says "you're not well yet!"

WHAT CAN I EXPECT? I ask!!!

I'm happy now! Surely there can't be better than this!

I'm not hurrying though - I'll just take each day as it comes. At least I'm not sky high any more! I've floated down a bit today.

I've noticed so many changes though I feel I've had all my birthdays at once: a lot happened Sunday & today.

For instance: 1) My nails are practically flat! It's so weird! And they're looking longer because of it.

2) My skin - believe it or not - is going like silk. They say its the cyclosporin! (One thing good about it!!)

3) My cheeks have really filled! AAGH.... That's due to Sundays + this mornings IV dose of Prednisolone.

4) My food SLIDES down my throat. Everything tastes so good.

5) I can BREATHE! Obvious eh:

6) My blackheads are ZILCH! And my skin on my face has gone really weird. It seems weird to me but they say it looks NORMAL!

7) My hands look different. They look colourful now and more defined. You'll see what I mean.

8) All my scars are healing really quick.

9) My voice is stronger. I can make them hear me in the corridor now but its deeper too. That helps.

10) I can lift myself up now with chest drains in.

11) I've so much energy. Every morning I wake up & just like Emma said, you feel like 6 again. Most odd.

12) I don't mind injections! Now, I must be ill but honestly, they're pricking me left, right + centre & I couldn't give a monkeys! Insulin, blood tests, thumb pricks.....etc.

13) My legs are colourful!! No longer white!

14) My lips are a really lovely pink colour & they feel really warm and lovely.

The list is endless. There's so many things. Everything is happening so fast though that I can't take it all in.

I got a lovely card off Sarah & Michael today. Sarah had drawn it & its made me laugh all day. Will you ring & tell her — them both — how much I love it. It says

And who's got

one...

then inside:

Its so good. I've shown it everyone! You've got to see it.

And who's got

one!

I've also been made an honoury member of The New heart Club in Horwich! A lovely letter off them. I got 38 cards this morning. inc. one or two letters. Dr Webb & co. sent me a large one covered in Butterflies!!! Remarkable! Norma & Arthur had butterflies too. Quite a few did. I opened one to you off Joy Everett by mistake — SORRY.

9.15 pm.   Jean has just left. I get on with her really well – we just
            never stop gabbing. I tell her how I coped with cf &
alsorts & she can't get over the number of similarities in food tastes
& everything that I have with Chris. She says he used to
go through hoards of fruit-pastilles too! I asked her if she
doesn't mind coming to see me & she feels it's helping her because
she has been able to see how good t/p's are and of the
benefits. She did admit she was nervous of meeting me to
talk to at first especially as she'd seen what I'd been through.
But, as she points out, we get on famously.
            I had my drain bucket changed earlier, at last. It had
finally fulled up !! They clamped the drains & told me to expect
a change in pressure. I waited, felt nothing, & that means
my lungs are finally almost ready!! Another 24hrs and
they're turning off the suction, then another 24 hrs and as
Dr Wallwork said to Scotty "Whip em out." (HELP!) I am
anxious but I'll just have to remember how well they've been
up to now.
            All my stitches up front 'itch'. They say that's the knitting
process!!   I had my other two drain stitches removed earlier.
YIPEE!. Two free! My wound's looking cleaner now & seems to
be healing well. Trouble is, I'm also feeling 'tight' as
they knit & this seems to be restricting my breathing.
            Jean brought me a mirror tonight – a large one – and I
burst into tears straight off.!! My face – all my cheeks – are puffed
up rounded. You really wouldn't believe it. But I look really
healthy. My colour is GREAT.
            (Before I forget. Thank Aunty Linda for Bonbons. Tell
her they're the best ones I've had in years as they slid down
once I'd chewed them. Trouble is, that many slid down and
the sugar slid up to 17. Guess who needed an injection!!!. Well
worth it though).
            Aunty Teri sent me a Gorgeous teddy today. He's
lovely. He's a nice blonde teddy colour with a big red bow. Not
named him yet! He arrived just as I discovered I'd not to
have a bronch. so he was like a bearer of good news!
            Scotty & the team walked in the room this morning
to find me snoozing & clutching old Goodfa to my chest
drain. I jumped up so fast, they didn't half all laugh.
They just storm in without warning !.
            Lancashire words are slowly creeping back into
this husky southern whisper, you'll be pleased to know!

And now, six months on, in the great event of my life, I am making plans. I no longer just live for today like I use to — I now look to the future once more. In september I am hoping to restart Art college and in the meantime I intend to concentrate on building up my wasted muscles. Slowly I am gaining my independence, and with it my confidence is growing. Transplantation takes a lot of adjusting to. "No one said it would be easy" reminded my parents when I returned home in January; and admittedly I have found it tough. But with each day I grow stronger and it's great to wake up each morning and feel healthy. As the dawn light floods my room and I wake each morning with a new-found energy and this alone gives me enough determination to fight for a brighter future.

Thanks to the skill and dedication of the surgeons who performed my operation, and to all those who prepared me beforehand and were able to organisize transport to take my heart 300 miles to another hospital to save another life, I am reminded each day as to why, this time last year, we turned to the media; so that we could let the public know that transplantation is marvellous surgery. Is it only a year since we asked for their support?

And to anyone who is still doubtful towards Transplant surgery let me tell you that last week I was lucky enough to meet the little boy who received my own heart. He is now a bright happy youngster of 11yeas old — no different than any other boy of his age. He enjoys football and spends hours riding his bike. Ask him yourself, and he will point out that now he is "pink all over! Just like you!"

But ironically, he was once that plum lipped, poorly little boy who was suffering from five major heart defects and, like so many other people today, he was dying....

Ask me, and I will say that a certain relative of mine was very wise when I told them that I had been put on Papworths active list.

For I am lucky!

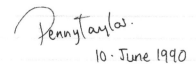

Penny Taylor.
10. June 1990

Penny's Thoughts on Transplantation

Left to Right: Penny with Jean after her transplant—Jean visited Penny every day while at Papworth.
Canon Reverend Paul Duffett with Penny on a previous visit—before the transplant.
Andrew Morley and Penny after the transplant.

To: THE BOLTON EVENING NEWS.

MALLARD WARD.
PAPWORTH.
28 November 1989.

Dear Sir,

Many, many thanks for publisising the latest news of my successful operation. I'm hoping it may help many people to realize that transplants are NOT an area of surgery which need to be feared. I'm so pleased that I never stopped believing in this operation because, now that I'm over it, I look back & realize it's the most beautiful experience I have ever encountered. I have enjoyed every minute of my recovery – it's been a whole new start for me, and I now realize how much transplants can improve a life. I have NEVER had it so good!

I would like to be able to tell the people of Bolton how good I really do feel. My mind is still too excited to sit and write another article about the whole thing, but I enclose a poem I wrote to my Aunty Margaret which sums up exactly what I have been through. So many people have sent their best wishes for my speedy recovery that I feel I owe it to them to let them know what it's all about. I realize it's a long poem but, if you should consider using it, I feel it comes across better in its entirety. (Maybe small print would suffice?)

In asking once more for your generous support may I please thank you for all the help you have offered in the past. (I think Bolton know what transplantation involves now!!)

Yours ever hopefully.

Penny.

Penny in Papworth hospital, with her family, teddies and cards.

Penny wrote this before her transplant. It was a wish come true.

I am a 20 year old victim of the disease Cystic Fibrosis, and have awaited a heart/lung transplant at Papworth Hospital, Cambridge, for 15 months. A donor became available in May this year, but during preparations for the operation, it was discovered that the organs were infected, and therefore unsuitable. A patient who was hoping to receive my heart was lucky enough to receive another suitable donor heart instead.

I do not wish anyone to die for my sake, but in the event of fatal accidents a vast source of donor organs are lost, simply because the possibility of them being prospective donors was never discussed, or even considered, during their lifetime.

Transplantation has already proved that it can extend, and improve, the lives of desperately ill patients.

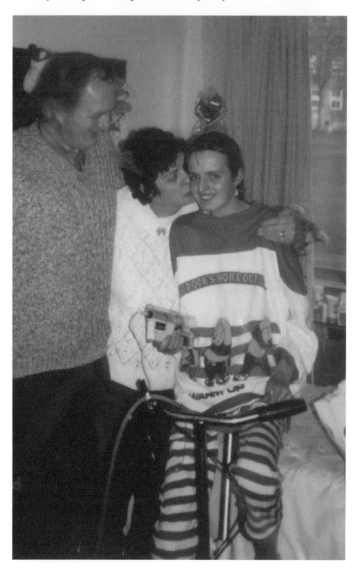

6. 8. 89.

Dear Penny,

I am a heart and lung transplant patient from Papworth and recently read your article with the Zipper Club Magazine, which impressed me enormously. It was so well written! In fact, I'm writing to ask you if you would mind it it were reprinted in my mother's church magazine (Withington Methodist Church). The people at the church have followed my decline in health and recent improvement (post-transplant) and I'm sure would be very interested to hear your story. Would it be alright?

I was terribly sorry to hear of your disappointing call (as were all my family). It was what I myself dreaded most. I wasn't so much afraid of the operation

WOODLAND recycled paper

as being told what you were. Fortunately for me, my call was the right one. I admire you greatly for the way you responded to your misfortune.

The main thing is not to give up hope! I can tell from your article that you have no intention of doing that but sometimes I found it helps just to know that people in the same situation have similar feelings. Sometimes, when I was very, very ill before the transplant I used to wonder if I would ever get the call, but deep down inside I was sure it would come.

I was suffering from primary pulmonary hypertension and in fact had my transplant just over a year ago. There is an incredible difference between me now and just before my transplant. Do you know any other transplant patients? If so, you'll know how it is. So set your sights on things you'll do when you're well! I've just come back from a holiday of walking in the mountains, which I used to dream of. You may not be able to do the things you wish immediately after the operation but with time you'll get there!

I do hope the right call comes very soon. My family and I are thinking of you and your family. Take care, Rosemary

Above: Penny, Andrew Walkden and Sean Walkden— cousins of Penny on John's side.

Friday, the 12th, should be GREAT. I go to see the voice surgeon in Manchester who is eager to get my voice done as he's only done the op. on terminally ill cancer patients & doesn't know what long term success rate is. (I may be shouting down your Telephone soon now!)

Post-Transplant

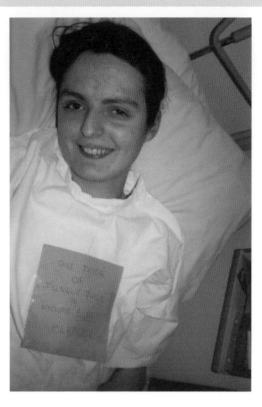

Above Left: A poster Penny created for her hospital door. Above Right: Penny at Papworth just after her transplants. Penny's doctors needed to look down her throat and into her lungs. This process, combined with an empty stomach was unpleasant, so Penny politely requested jungle juice for numbing purposes.

John, Hannah, Andrew Morley, Anita Duffett, Penny, Judith and Paul Duffett. Penny got to know Paul Duffett very well as he was Papworth's chaplain. When Penny had to have part of her lung removed, the Duffetts housed Andrew, John and Judith for three weeks. Rev Paul Duffett also assisted at Penny's funeral. Anita cooked for John, Andrew and Judith and did so much for us all.

PENELOPE SUSAN (Penny) TAYLOR
DRUGS LIST 5th JANUARY 1991

ANTI REJECTION DRUGS:-

Cyclosporin 100 mg.	6 per day
Cyclosporin 25 mg.	6 per day
Azathioprine 25 mg.	1 per day
Prednisolone 1 mg.	3 per day
Prednisolone 5 mg.	1 per day

ANTIBIOTICS:-

Acyclovir 800 mg.	4 per day
Septrin	1 tablet twice weekly

PANCREATIN SUPPLEMENT:-

Creon Capsules (depending on type and amount of food)8 to 12 per day

EXTRA DRUGS:-

Frusemide 40 mg.	1 tablet daily
Ranitidine 150 mg.	2 tablets daily
Potassium Chloride S/R (Slow-K) 600Mg.	2 tablets daily
Quinine Sulphate 300 mg.	1 tablet daily
Norethisterone Tablets 5 mg.	3 tablets daily
Ephedrine Nasal drops 0.5% (10ml.)	2 drops twice daily
Vibramycin Tablets 100mg	1 tablet per day

Since transplantaion, blood glucose levels have to be tested and
treated if necessary using the following:-

B.M. test 1-44	50 per box
Unilet A.T. 0502 glucose (for use with glucolet) 200 per box	
Human Mixtard 30/70 100 units per ml.	
Human Actrapid	
Micro-fine IV 0.5ml Sterile Insulin Syringes	

The following are for a period of three weeks from 22.12.90
INTRAVENOUS DRUGS:-

Ceftazidime	3gramms	4 times daily
0.9% Sodium Chloride Intravenous Solution 100 ml. bag		4 per day
0.9% Sodium Chloride Intravenous Solution 50 ml. bag		1 per day
5 ml.Hepsal Sterile Heparinised Saline 10 units per vial		4 per day
Water for injection	20 ml. plastic vials	4 per day
Giving sets		1 per day
Syringe	5 ml.	4 per day
Syringe	10 ml.	4 per day
Green needles		4 per day
White needles (micro lance 19G2)		4 per day
Sterets	(cleaning swabs)	8 per day
Vygon 88600	(white plugs)	6 per day
B Braun	(red plugs)	6 per day
Parama	(4 metre bandages)	1 per day
Micropore tape		

'Sister Arthur' and her husband with Penny. She had met Penny at Bolton District Hospital Outpatients and made a surprise visit to Penny at Papworth.

Penny at Papworth with a cuppa.

Penny and Sarah Whatmore at Papworth. Sarah and Penny were great friends till the end.

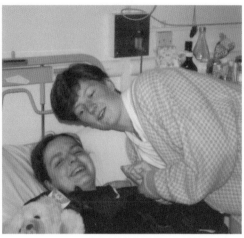

Penny and Michele after the transplant at Papworth. Michele opened a café at this point in her life so time spent with Penny was very precious to them both.

Aunties and uncles who were support for Judith and John. Judith's sister Barbara, Auntie Betty's mum, Auntie Betty, Uncle Bert, Bert's wife Auntie Ann, Uncle Dave (Auntie Betty's husband), and Judith.

Penny with John Duckworth and his parents at Papworth. Kath and Les had supported Penny since she was very young. They would take food to hospital and visited her regularly. They always had lots of laughs.

Penny Leaves Us

At 8.45pm on 20th January 1992, Penny peacefully went to sleep having told John and I to get out on our bikes and be happy.

On 27th January her funeral was held in Horwich Parish Church in accordance with her wishes. The service was led by Rev Gatenby assisted by Rev Paul Duffett (the Chaplain at Papworth) and the Curate of Horwich Parish Church, Johnathon Carmyllie, who read the poem 'White Coppice' that Penny had written and dedicated to her fiancé, Andrew Morley. So many people attended the service that her friends had to sit in the choir stalls. One friend in particular, Sharon, was fighting a losing battle to pull her very short skirt down towards her knees. Despite the solemnity of the occasion it made me smile as I could imagine how funny Penny would have found this. Family friends had prepared a buffet in church for people who chose not to attend the internment. Others attended Ridgmont Cemetery for the burial service.

The day after the funeral, John and I went to stay in my cousin's house in St Andrews. It gave us the opportunity to grieve alone and come to terms with our loss. Taking Penny's advice, we spent time on our bikes and took solace in the peace and quiet of time alone. Penny had written the poem 'Sleepers Shore' shortly before her passing, and when she knew that her time had almost come. It is a beautiful reminder of the girl she was.

SLEEPERS SHORE

I'm so, so near the sleepers shore

Yet still my body fights for more,

Why is this world so hard to leave?

Is it to curb my friends sad grieve?

Or is it merely love of life

That makes it hard to leave this strife?

I know not what the answer is –

But joy is such that only life can give

So maybe that is why I fight for more

And cannot cross the sleepers shore.

My body's weak but my mind is strong

And so I still for earthly pleasures long,

But if my body suddenly breaks

I feel assured that I will wake

Amongst the friends I know so fond –

Those friends who wait in Gods beyond

Penny Taylor 24/06/69-20/01/92

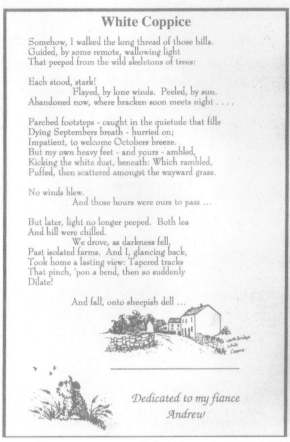

White Coppice

Somehow, I walked the long thread of those hills.
Guided, by some remote, wallowing light
That peeped from the wild skeletons of trees:

Each stood, stark!
       Flayed, by lone winds. Peeled, by sun.
Abandoned now, where bracken soon meets night . . . .

Parched footsteps - caught in the quietude that fills
Dying Septembers breath - hurried on;
Impatient, to welcome Octobers breeze.
But my own heavy feet - and yours - ambled,
Kicking the white dust, beneath: Which rambled,
Puffed, then scattered amongst the wayward grass.

No winds blew.
       And those hours were ours to pass …

But later, light no longer peeped. Both lea
And hill were chilled.
       We drove, as darkness fell,
Past isolated farms. And I, glancing back,
Took home a lasting view: Tapered tracks
That pinch, 'pon a bend, then so suddenly
Dilate!

    And fall, onto sheepish dell …

Dedicated to my fiance
Andrew

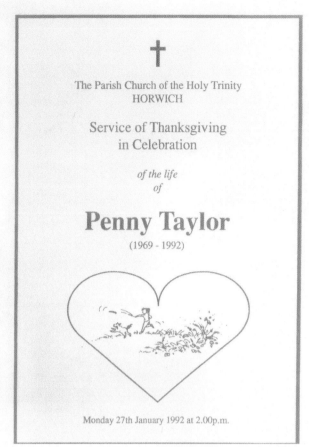

✝

The Parish Church of the Holy Trinity
HORWICH

Service of Thanksgiving
in Celebration

of the life
of

Penny Taylor

(1969 - 1992)

Monday 27th January 1992 at 2.00p.m.

Chorus
Dance, then, wherever you may be;
I am the Lord of the Dance, said he,
And I'll lead you all, wherever you
may be,
And I'll lead you all in the dance,
said he.

1
I danced in the morning
  when the world was begun,
And I dance in the moon
  and the stars and the sun,
And I came down from heaven
  and I danced on the earth;
At Bethlehem
  I had my birth:

2
I danced for the scribe
  and the pharisee,
But they would not dance
  and they wouldn't follow me;
I danced for the fishermen,
  James and John;
They came with me
  and the dance went on:

3
I danced on the Sabbath
  and I cured the lame:
The holy people
  said it was a shame.
They whipped and they stripped
  and they hung me high,
And they left me there
  on a cross to die:

4
I danced on a Friday
  when the sky turned black;
It's hard to dance
  with the devil on your back.
They buried my body
  and they thought I'd gone;
But I am the dance
  and I still go on:

5
They cut me down
  and I leap up high;
I am the life
  that'll never, never die;
I'll live in you
  if you live in me:
I am the Lord
  of the Dance, said he:

The Address

THE READING
Isaiah 40 verses 27 - end

The Prayers

"White Coppice"

1
Who would true valour see,
  Let him come hither;
One here will constant be,
  Come wind, come weather;
There's no discouragement
Shall make him once relent
His first avowed intent
  To be a pilgrim.

2
Whoso beset him round
  With dismal stories,
Do but themselves confound;
  His strength the more is.
No lion can him fright,
He'll with a giant fight,
But he will have the right
  To be a pilgrim.

3
No goblin nor foul fiend
  Can daunt his spirit;
He knows he at the end
  Shall life inherit.
Then, fancies, fly away;
He'll not fear what men say;
He'll labour night and day
  To be a pilgrim.

This service is followed by interment at Ridgmont Cemetery.
Light refreshments will be available in church for those who remain
in church and also on return from the Cemetery. *Please join us.*

Penny's funeral Service of Thanksgiving—designed by Penny herself.

Tributes to Penny

THE BRITISH CARDIAC PATIENTS ASSOCIATION

REGISTERED CHARITY NO: 289190

PAPWORTH TRANSPLANTS

President: Sir Terence English P.R.C.S.
Vice-President: Mr. Ben Milstein. M.A. F.R.C.S.
Executive Vice President: Mr Fred Roach

T-PLANTERS

NEWSLETTER No: 38

April 1992

Dear Friends.

In the February 'T'-Planter I published one of the many poems by Penny Taylor whose poems and articles have given so much pleasure to our readers for over two and a half years. The poem, "Forgotten Key", was written by Penny on 5th December 91 and was printed in the 'T'-Planter in mid-January for distribution in February. Shortly afterwards I received the sad news that Penny had died on 20th January and it was the wish of Penny's parents that the printed newsletter should go ahead unaltered. I am sure you will wish to join me in offering our sincere condolences and thanks to Judith & John.

Penny's writing comforted and encouraged so many people and right to the end she maintained a positive and cheerful attitude. In keeping with that fine spirit may I offer, as a tribute to Penny, the following lines:

THE YEARS WITH CHANGE ADVANCE:

IF I MAKE DARK MY COUNTENANCE,

I SHUT MY LIFE FROM HAPPIER CHANCE.

Alfred Lord Tennyson

*   *   *   *   *

PENNY

Penny was so brave right to the end

Always so cheerful, everyone's friend

She had such wonderful parents too

Sharing and caring a real happy "crew"

You have nothing to reproach yourselves for

No loving couple could have done more

Penny was fun loving, witty and bright

Against her illness she put up such a fight

I'm sure there's a heaven somewhere out there

Where Penny's relaxing without a care

So don't cry and don't despair

For Penny is happy in God's Tender Care

Marge xxx

Penny's memory

BRAVE Penny Taylor of Horwich may have died at only 22, but she will not be forgotten. Her struggle and courage before and after her heart-lung transplant a couple of years ago was an inspiration to many.

She never accepted that she was particularly brave, and her bright outlook on life was evident even in some of her poems which appeared in our Poet's Corner.

Our sympathy goes to her parents and boyfriend Andrew. But in their sadness, perhaps they can be helped by the thought that in Penny's short life she made more impact on those around her than most people do in their three score years and ten.

From Bolton Evening News.

Penny after her transplant with Fred Roach, the editor of the newsletter above. He kept in contact with Penny and visited her in Papworth.

5th January 1987

Death should never be feared, for it is like life.

When we are born we have no knowledge of what lies in front of us. We are naked warriors travelling into the unknown. But we are prepared! We survive!

In times of uncertainty we are guided. In times of weakness we find strength. When we feel alone we find comfort and assurance and thus overcome our insecurities.

Why then should we fear such a natural occurrence such as death?

We are by this time, wiser, and have come to realise that always there are reasons, and guidance. We should learn to accept that there is far more to life than <u>living</u>. We all know that we are naked in death as we are in birth. So perhaps we should view 'life' as a learning process; a preparation for an even greater knowledge. We come prepared for life, so surely life prepares us for death!

Penny Taylor
24.06.1969-20.01.1992

THE AMBASSADRESS ANGEL.

What can be said about PENNY ?
It's really quite hard to explain.
She brought love and joy to so many,
Even though she suffered such pain.

We can't understand why God chose her,
When she should have been in her prime,
In the dark moments we miss her, we ask:
"How could He commit such a crime ?"

But God had been watching young PENNY,
All the wonderful poetry and art,
And He thought to Himself:
"How I need this young girl,
Before all the world falls apart."

"She will be my Ambassadress Angel.
She will fly out all over the earth.
Give the world a new hue,
Paint the sky once more blue,
Help me in its re-birth."

God healed all the wounds in her body,
Commanding she feel whole again,
So she breathed in the sweet air of
                                    heaven,
Giving joy that there was no fierce pain.

God told her of the new mission,
All the wonderful things she would do,
And brave PENNY said: "Give me brushes
                            and paints,
And a pencil and writing pad too!"

We all know that PENNY will succeed,
Her whole life was a pure inspiration,
To all those who knew of her courage
                            and faith,
In the face of such cruel devastation.

Her precious love is a gift to us all,
Cherished always inside the heart.
Remembering PENNY will light up our lives,
So we never need feel far apart.

THE
AMBASSADRESS
ANGEL.

Helen Robinson Pollitt.
Monday 20th January
        1992.

FOR PENNY.

"She will reach powerful leaders in their
                                    dreams,
And whisper her beautiful verse,
That they may forget all their devious
                                    schemes,
Before making the world any worse."

"She will help those in pain and in sorrow,
She will comfort and restore their hope.
Give them courage in facing tomorrow,
Give them strength so that they may cope.

"Her laughter she'll share with all people,
Bring them happiness in every day,
Help them to enjoy their time on this earth,
Before I must take them away!"

So God reached down and touched our young
                                    PENNY,
And took her back to His home,
There she met all the loved ones who'd
                        left her behind,
So she never would be all alone.

So unfurl your golden wings PENNY,
Soar into the heavenly sky,
On the darkest of nights we will
                        follow your star,
A glittering brilliance seen from
                                    afar,
Will colour our lives,
An incredible hue,
Shining with special memories of
                                    you.

HORWICH Rector Canon Denis Gatenby paid tribute to the enormous courage of heart-lung swap girl Penny Taylor at the funeral service yesterday celebrating her life.

Penny, who suffered from cystic fibrosis, died last week, aged 22, and had planned her own funeral asking that no one should mourn or be saddened by her death.

The service was held at Horwich Parish Church conducted by Canon Gatenby entitled A Service of Thanksgiving in Celebration of Her Life featuring a poem she had written dedicated to her fiance Andrew.

As a committed Christian Penny, of Church Street, Horwich, drew strength from her faith and in turn was a source of inspiration to her family and many friends.

Source

Canon Gatenby who had discussed with her the scriptures and faith said at the service she ible in requesting people not to be saddened by her death.

He told the family and friends which included parents Judith and John: "What we are doing is something very different from the usual concept of a funeral service.

"It is a celebration — a celebration of a life lived to the full and one in which she achieved so much, a celebration of her great courage and above all a celebration of its source Jesus Christ."

He added: "If when my time comes and your time comes you can go with the same dignity and confidence as she did, her living and her dying would not have been in vain."

The service was followed by a internment at Ridgmont Cemetery.

Bolton Evening News

Penny

Truly an angel, a brief glimpse of heaven,
Never heard to complain, or resent.
Always cheerful, patient, accepting,
A shining example to all where she went.

—

Our privilege to have known her, an inspiration,
She helped in so many ways.
From aiding me through my operation
To inspiring me through my worst days.

—

A true friend to my son has she been
There will never be her like again.
For saints are rare in this day and age,
So few so pure and free from stain.

—

GOD BLESS HER

WE SHALL NEVER FORGET HER

REMEMBERED WITH LOVE

Kathleen.

From: Rt.Revd. David Galliford
Mrs Claire Galliford

Bishops Garth
Maltongate
Thornton-le-Dale
North Yorkshire YO18 7SA

11. 2. 92

Dear Mr & Mrs Taylor,

When I was in Manchester yesterday I heard the news of Penny's death, so I felt I must send you a word.

Penny was an inspiration to many for her courage, tenacity, and cheerfulness. That will have been said to you on all sides I am sure, and it will be some comfort to you in your great loss.

Many people will be thinking especially of you both at this time since you carried the burden of those trips up and down to Cambridgeshire and the care and attention you gave to Penny in between at home.

It moved me very much to think of all you had done for her and her very courageous life -

This brings kind wishes and to say I know you will find a great deal of support from friends and others like me for the days ahead. God bless you very much.

Yours sincerely
David Galliford

APPENDIX 1: People in Penny's Life
Sarah Justin

Sarah and I met in September 1987. We shared a room in Monsall Hospital, Manchester, in ward 15. Neither of us were organized so our room soon resembled the local tip. Magazines were piled onto every available chair and a fold up table stood in one corner. This held the edibles which we tucked into during the day. We didn't much care for the food that was served at mealtimes so our 'supplies' were a blessing. Our room also contained a T.V - (colour aswell!) - a video and a computer on which we played 'magic mushrooms' or 'Pacman'. We both shared similar interests too so we had plenty to talk about. She lives in Macclesfield though, so this means that we don't get to see each other often. I live in Bolton, so the easiest way to keep in touch is to write.

SARAH.

I resolved to help her to smile,
From the moment I woke in the
Early hours to hear her woeful
Cry.

And in return she gave me
So much! She taught me how to fight
For my life. Before - finally -
She proudly taught me how to die.

Penny Taylor.
6ᵗʰ July 1989.

Sarah Justin and her mum. Sarah was a fellow CF sufferer. She and Penny met while sharing a room in Monsall Hospital and they quickly became very good friends. Penny was utterly devastated at Sarah's passing while awaiting transplant.

Heaven Sent, Taylor Made

'That's Life'. BBC Television. LONDON

68. Church St.
HORWICH.
BOLTON. Lancs.
15 June 1989.

Dear 'That's Life',

Life, for a 20 year old girl in Monsall Hospital, Manchester, at present, is very bleak. You see, my friend Sarah Justin has been on the ward now for six weeks and each day she is growing more weaker due to the disease Cystic Fibrosis. Hers, is not an uncommon situation, as you are well aware of. But Sarah has been on Papworths heart and lung transplant waiting list now since January and still a donor has not been found. She weighs a meagre 4 stones 12 ounces and she desperately needs a transplant very soon.

I have known Sarah for almost two years, though when I first met her she looked very frail and blue, due to the lack of oxygen in her blood. But I soon discovered that Sarah is a fighter and despite the rough periods of these past 2 years, she always fights back. I have no doubt that she will still continue to fight but her need for the transplant is suddenly far more desperate. I was permitted to see her yesterday for the first time since last month and though I've written to her, I had no idea just how ill she is. I very nearly cried to see her tiny withdrawn face, and throughout the time I was with her I felt so utterly helpless. It broke my heart to see her.

I _am_ helpless in that there is absolutely nothing I am able to do other than to keep writing in order to keep her spirits up. She has given me so much strength over these two years and I feel unable to do anything to help her or to ease her suffering.

The only thing to do, I thought, is to open the eyes of the public once more and plead .. yes plead .. to them for their much needed support in signing donor cards.

All the efforts you made last year should not be suddenly cast aside and forgotten! Last years publicity should only have been the START of making the public more aware, of how vital transplant surgery really is. One look at Sarah is enough to confirm this, and I know how much she could benefit if only someone were to give her the chance.

Perhaps you could read this letter out on your programme. Surely something can be done to raise the public interest once more. But I am unable to do this alone - this is why I write to you for your help. Please do something.

I am also awaiting a heart/lung transplant at Papworth Hospital, and I have waited since last July, so I can understand what Sarah is going through. We are both of the same age and both have Cystic Fibrosis. It is no longer just a "life threatening childrens disease", it has become an "unneccessary adults disease" too. Transplant surgery won't cure cystic fibrosis, but it is being treated now as another form of treatment. It is the most beneficial treatment for this disease, and research into this area of surgery can only improve if people, myself included, are willing to undergo surgery.

I am very optimistic about the future for both Sarah and myself, but unless we are granted this unique opportunity to live like any other average human being, our time is running out. We don't WANT the donor to die, but dying is the most natural inevitability of living. If others are able to benefit, surely their death will not have been a total waste. Perhaps those who do not believe, or agree with, transplant surgery, have never had to watch many of their young friends die.

Sarah and I have promised to do our own Christmas shopping this year and spend a whole day walking around Manchester, and we are determined to do so. But this could be an unlikely dream without your help, and public interest.

'Whilst we breathe, we hope'.

Your sincerely.
Miss Penny Taylor.

Death, awaits us all. And I shall leave my friends.
But first, upon this fine land that lends
Its glory to secret valleys, springs, and hills
Where lie the timid beasts; the flowers: and moan
The captured winds; I shall roam.
My mind will rest awhile amongst the daffodils,
And the soft, scented murmurings of nymphs shall forever
Dwell in my breast.
And there will never
Be a sight more lovely, or complete, than
The firm swellings of Earth; these ancient grassy mounds
Upon which our ancestors began.
And all those aged sports! The fox. And hounds
With teeth, and snarl, and steadfast run.
Followed, by the urgent sounds of man and horse!
Where now - upon this beaten course -
Nettles and leaves sprawl endlessly. And high, the golden sun.

Blissful Wanderings.

27th February 1989.

Bic (40 mins)

MONDAY 26TH JUNE 1989. 10·10 pm.

Sarah Justin was on this programme, 26th June 1989. She was filmed during her assessment in January 1989.

The previous night, 25th June, her brother Paul was on "That's Life" appealing for more people to sign donor cards and to talk about it with their families. I had written to "That's Life" every day from 19th June and Paul had rung & written to them. On the Friday, 23rd, they invited him onto that weeks show. He appeared on "That's Life", starring Esther Rantzen, with Transplant patients Jo Beetles, Jo Chittock & Julie Bennett, all CF.

Sadly Sarah died, aged 20, on 28th June 1989. Three days after Paul's appearance on "That's Life".

Penny, with Sarah, November 1988.

Dear Perry,

the thankyou at the top of the page is first of all to thank you, your Mum and Dad, and of course Freeway for making us so welcome last Sunday and giving us such a wonderful time (which we have not stopped talking about all week). Secondly it is to thank you for waiting so long for a letter from me, who is not the most punctual of letter writers (ha!) to say the least. It has been so long that to forgive me at all deserves merit.

Monday 21st March 1988

Well, what have I done since last week? – Not alot! Watching the rain fall and counting the clouds. (One – all over the rotten sky!). In the end I thought I would have a go at poetry, my attempt at this will be revealed in the future (oh no!), along with other things (!!!). Fear the worst.

This afternoon we are going to Morsall holiday camp, because last time we went we enjoyed it so much we thought we would go again as soon as possible..... no that's not entirely true as you probably suspected. The real reason is that I have been having trouble with swollen ankles again and we want to make sure I'm not pregnant, as this would be very awkward.

My current book choice is "A Passage to India" and I am thinking of going there! Care to come with me? – Don't answer that! I hope you are doing well with "Tess"; just think of me when you read the sub-title, no doubt you will agree it is very apt. My book has gone nowhere as usual though my ideas are still budding. If I write at the rate I write to you it should be finished in twenty years time?! (At least). And of course I shall ask you to illustrate it for me. So you can look forward to a nice job (or – doing me a favor) in old age.

Well, I shall have to go now as I think someone is banking in downstairs. Keep well, and thank you, again!

luv Sarah.

xxx.

December 4th 1987

Dear Penny,

Please, please, please forgive me for not having written(?) sooner only I thought it I had you would have died of boredom by the second line, which incidentally would have been the end of the letter as nothing remotely interesting has happened to me since I last saw you. I am at last, though, out of the old prisoner of war camp, I'm sure you know where I mean.

No, I'm not back at college, but of course am working incredibly hard to keep things up here(!). Perhaps I should set my sights on after Christmas and not be so hasty. I hope you are doing well, working hard and not finding the work too easy. which I know can be very frustrating. (ha!)

How is your book going? Are you any closer to getting it published? My masterpiece is as yet unfinished. Sadly. You will probably hear more about it when I am nominated for the Nobel Prize for literature next year. Or some similar nomination. (Macclesfields under seven's short story award!)

Lets hang out at your place!

Enough of that. I know I shall make you green with envy if I go on. How is Freeway? After Christmas we shall be getting another dog. (I say "shall be", but it is still "may be"), from the dogs home. Do not ask me the reason for this.

Well if you're not asleep already I salute you. No news from this end. Hope you have a wonderful holiday, and just go easy on the alcohol at Yuletide! Remember me to your family.

Hope to here from you soon.

your friend

Sarah

x

P.S. Please excuse my spelling mistakes and awful layout. I am sending you a photograph of my dog Sam (soon to be 'jdread) so you can see what he's like (thrill)

Restive illustrations.(?) (as you can see I had only three pens. I hope you are not worried by the competition)

peace. (mind you I can hardly complain about the mess, state of my bedroom. Last time I was in hospital Dr Webo said I had... ... Well, let us say he thought I made myself at home.) The old place needs a good tidy up though. (I'll anyone finds this letter I'm done for!). I actually gave my verdict on how the bathroom should be done and to my utter amazement they actually rang the plumber to discuss it with him. I was praised for my good idea and common sense, till it was discovered that to do it my way would mean to relinquish the door to the bathroom or would all the washbasin! Incredible but true!. Suffice to say they have ③

not asked for my advise since. Anyway won't keep you with my drivel any longer.
Good luck in Prison, Please let me know when they sentence you!
Tally ho!
Sarah
xx.

P.S. Hope you and your folks are all happy and healthy.
P.P.S. I really hope they don't sentence you, and if they do retire the new syringes.

Wednesday 13th April '88

28, Ryles Park road
Macclesfield
Cheshire
Sk11 8RH

Dear Perry,
Hopefully when you get this you should be out and about and have all loose ends tied up. Sorry for not writing when you were in hospital only I wasn't sure when you were actually 'in' or out, or if you went home for a few days etc. The day after seeing you I had an attack of the old pleurisy so was laid up for a few days, all the excitement I suppose (?). 'Bit of a panic as you can imagine, Ah, well at least you managed to escape me!

However, now I am devoting all my energy into reading hard and trying to catch up on my list. Discovering what a pessimist Philip Larkin is. His temperament suits the time just now. And Blyton is proving hard going, do you have any tips? And I could do with some help on Beartrix Potter.

Today I had a new quilt cover. This is perhaps as well because "Sarah Kay" at my age is a bit much. The wombles pillocase will just have to go, it is simply not good enough. Then again it does seem a shame. Maybe I could have them under-neath, what do you think?

As we went to Haworth to see the Brontë's place the next "bookish" town on the map is to be Bath I think, or perhaps Stratford. If we are both well at the same time (!!!) maybe you could come with us. What say you? No-one knows about it yet (if you know what I mean) so just keep it in mind. I think given the choice they would rather take you than me! Nevertheless Patsy might be easier prey. Anyway it is early days yet, do not worry about it.

Chickened out of going to see "Fatal Attraction" as I thought it would be too violent, ("Noddy goes to the Circus" is too violent for me!) "The Last Emperor" does not look too bad or "Cry Freedom" but they both look a bit "iffy". Yes, I know I'm a coward.

absolute { "Well, must depart - with my energetic action - packed life i can hardly spare a minute" } "drivel".

thankyou for your
        time, (and perseverance)
        love from,
        Sarah J.

you can make
a mountain out of my molehill anytime.

Heaven Sent, Taylor Made

Penny and Sarah corresponded regularly…

Tuesday 10 Jan 89 -

SEND THE BUGS PACKING!

Hi Sarah!

I was going to write this letter in BIG PRINT as I thought you might be so tired you may not be able to read it. However, perhaps your mum or Dad will read it to you if this is the case.

How was the journey down - hope you found it easily. It's my bet that you had a shock when you saw the place - nothing like what we'd expected when we first went there.

Have you seen the sign on entering Papworth village?

Quite appropriate seeing as those who first visit the place are usually in bad shape. I think they should have another sign at the other end of the village which states:

By now, undoubtedly, you will have met Peg! No, that's not one of the auxillaries - I'm talking about the good old nose peg- KNOW WHAT I MEAN!!
(Awful isn't it)

I mean, how on earth are you expected to take deep breaths with a confounded nose peg on! As if breathing isn't difficult enough to start with !!*?!!

The tardis is good isn't it - I quite liked that test - probably because its not as tiring as the other lung function tests.
Have you seen any transplant patients yet? I said to mum imagine if they send for me this week and whilst in Intensive Care they said to you "here's a patient who's just had a transplant" - you'd have quite a shock no doubt.

watch out for daleks!

I went out for an afternoon outing yesterday - to Monsall. (Perhaps you've heard of it. It's just near Manchester and lots of people go there for their holidays. The food's not too good but they do brilliant impersonations of dishwashes with their cups of tea!") You'll have to have a holiday there sometime (ONLY KIDDING) - Ward 15 (oops - I mean Chalet 15) and ... Chalet 7... are doing cheap holidays for CFs at the moment. Everyone goes to 15 if they want to play pool and they're even allowed to use the kitchen facilities too. All the rooms in 15 are 'private' though there is one double room - it's really quite exclusive and à la poshe! Adam and Matthew (the brothers) are on 15 as well as Mark Burgess and John Bolton. My pal Stephen, from Fleetwood, is on 7 with Antony and 'whats is name' with the earrings and leather jacket. I think you'll know who I mean. As you can see, its one of the more popular holiday resorts.

    I had an X-ray too (yes. they even take your photo as a souviner of the holiday). All's well with the old wheeze bags so I don't have to go again till NEXT WEDNESDAY !! This reminds me, I had a scan at Papworth for my heart and guess what - they couldn't find it! However, medical experts are 99.9% sure that I almost certainly have one, so I've not to worry. Its there somewhere. Apparently its the lungs that hide it.

    Freeway says "Hello"!! As you'll notice he's been clipped out again so he looks something like this at the moment.

    Michele and Ryan are coming over tomorrow. Ryan walked on his own for the 1st time on Monday - he looks about 18 mths yet he's only 10 mths.

    On the 19th I've got a ticket for the play "To kill a Mockingbird" - its a brill book so I hope the plays as good. I bought Andrew a ticket as his Christmas present so luckily he can do the driving. He's an advanced driver so we should get there in one piece. Mum said that John Bolton was asking her about the advanced driving in view of taking it himself and she was saying to him how you have to check your mirror every 5 seconds. He replied that he's used to doing that as he's always checking to see if the Police are following him !!!

    All is peaceful here just now. Mum has gone over to her friend Norma's for a gossip. Dad's at work. Freeway has gone in his basket (he's never been one

Printed in Great Britain
by Amazon

Spring is Coming, Jesse!

by
Jane Hurley

In memory of Jesse. Thank you boy for the happy times.

for writing letters) and the house is lovely & quiet for once - The district nurse called this morning with one of those soft mattresses. Papworth said as I'd lost weight on my hips then this would be ideal and would avoid bedsores so they suggested we got one to try out. They put one on my bed whilst I was there and it was amazingly comfy.

Q: whats this?

A: Me running out of News!
(or is it a News flash!)

Anyhow. I'd better finish this letter before the jokes get really bad. I wouldn't want to damage your health even further.

I shall be keeping my fingers crossed for you!!
(in fact we all are)

See you soon!
Love
Penny.
×
(and parents, & driveway) Jo

PHOTO OF DUCKPOND & SURGICAL WARDS

Surgical Wards at Papworth
(the duck ponds n'lie isn't it)

Have you seen the sign on the surgical ward door — "Please keep the door shut to keep the warmth in and the Ducks out". What a menu they could come up with with a bit of effort ie, Duck Pâté; Duck a l'orange; Duck soup; etc.

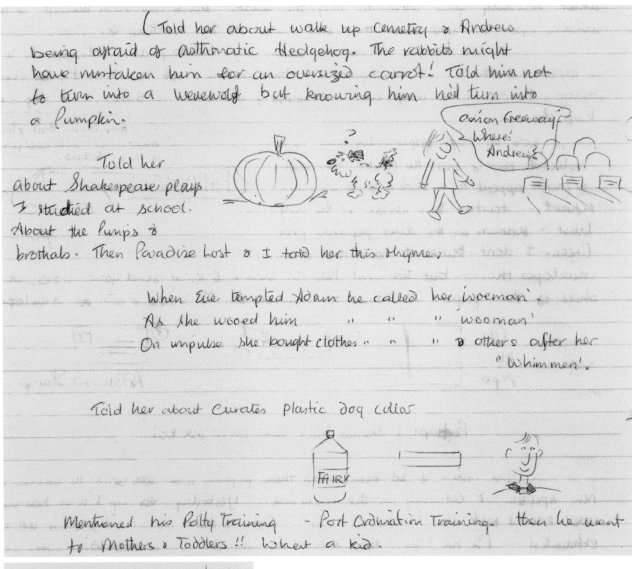

(Told her about walk up cemetry & Andrew being afraid of asthmatic Hedgehog. The rabbits might have mistaken him for an oversized carrot! Told him not to turn into a werewolf but knowing him he'd turn into a Pumpkin.

Told her about Shakespeare plays I studied at school. About the Pumps & brothals. Then Paradise Lost & I told her this rhyme.

When Eve tempted Adam he called her 'woeman'.
As she wooed him "   "   " 'wooman'
On impulse she bought clothes " "   " & others after her
                                        " Whimmen'.

Told her about Curates plastic dog collar

Mentioned his Potty Training - Post Ordination Training then he went to Mothers & Toddlers !! What a kid.

Penny and Sarah would often write about issues that non CF sufferers wouldn't think anything of.

The snippet below is from one of Sarah's letters to Penny in which she bemoans perfume wearers. CF sufferers would often be very affected by scents.

The illustration is of Penny's Auntie Margaret who had to remove her perfume at Penny's house! See more in a couple of pages.

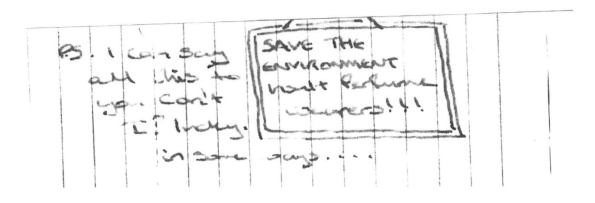

Letters to Sarah's family following Sarah's death.

68 Church Street.
Horwich. BOLTON.
21 September 1989.

Dear Paul,

I write to you because I can never find the words I wish to say on the phone. I don't want this letter to upset you, though no doubt just hearing from me will serve as a reminder to the loss that you will be still trying to come to terms with.

I don't suppose I am able to offer many words of comfort either, because I can't even begin to imagine how you must be feeling. But I want you to remember that the hurt that you feel in your own heart, is present in mine too. And though you perhaps feel alone with this hurt, maybe you will gain a little reassurance in knowing that you are not alone. There have been, and there will continue to be, instances in which I have been reminded of Sarah ; - sometimes, things happen that I would love to tell her about, and it makes me feel so numb inside when I realise that I can no longer phone, or write to her. Many times I miss not being able to just chat to her.

Somehow though, life goes on now, doesn't it!

Maybe we ought to be picking up those far, scattered pieces of lifes complex puzzle!

I don't know about you, but I am finding it truly difficult to know where to begin. How do you reconstruct a 'puzzle' that suddenly, so tragically, has a vital piece missing? A piece that has centred in your lives for so long.

May I offer my thoughts? My own theory is that it will never be possible. How can it be! The puzzle will always remain incomplete.

So let me suggest a solution for what remains of this puzzle. It is a solution which won't promise to ease the pain - (for that, I have no answer) - but it may help you to reconstruct the other pieces :

Take each piece, each area of your life, and consider them all carefully. (Allow a lot of time, and a great deal of patience!) Then, when you have done this, try to reassemble each piece in a different way - never allowing the missing piece to stray far from your mind. Always allow yourself to think about this missing piece; never try to block it from your mind. If the missing piece makes you feel that you want to cry, then cry freely. Likewise, should happiness fill your heart by thinking of this missing piece, then laugh! Never ignore what your heart feels most, because by releasing these feelings you will release with them a little of the frustration and hurt

Eventually, the 'puzzle' will once again be complete. It will never be the same as it was before, and you will always remember how it was previously, but maybe one day you will feel confident enough to put the past to one side, and find courage to add new pieces of your own to lifes ever-complex puzzle.

I know this may seem a very confusing way of explaining my own ideas, but perhaps (if you're not already confused!) you will give it some thought and try to understand my meaning.

It is the only way I can explain my theory, and I intend to put this theory into practice myself. Only time will say whether or not it has worked.

I won't say much more now - words are the hardest things to construct when you try to express the way you feel! And I have no wish to upset you any more than perhaps I already have.

You have lost your sister; I have lost a good friend.

It hurts beyond words!

But always remember that you will never be alone in this loss. And we'll both have our own ways, our own time, in coming to terms with this loss.

However, I sincerely hope that we can both - in a future moment - feel that we have gained maturity, understanding, or whatever it might be, from having known Sarah. Maybe, in later years, the missing piece of the puzzle will be replaced, simply because we loved her.

For now though, we ought to allow the hurt to bide it's time in it's familiar manner, and hope that with each day it will continue to hurt less than it does now.

Please give my love to your Mum and Dad, and never forget that you all remain in our thoughts and prayers.

I hope you don't mind that I have written to you like this, so unexpectedly, but it has helped me to put my own thoughts into some sort of perspective, and I hope it will help you in the same way.

With much love and encouragement,
Penny.
x

68 Church Street.
Horwich. BOLTON.
30th June 1989.

Dear Brian, Beryl and Paul,

To describe the feelings shared between two people, who are victims to the same illness, is very difficult. Sarah and I were lucky as we were able to understand how the other felt, and because we shared similar symptoms it became considerably easier for us to cope with them. To discover that we both experienced a bleeding lung, or a familiar 'burning sensation' following yet another coughing session, made these symptoms seem far less serious. No-one else is able to identify with these symptoms in this way, and I should imagine that it must have been a lot more frustrating for you to see Sarah poorly, than it was for me. Not that this makes it any easier to cope with - the hurt remains equally for us all and, having seen her recently, I feel that the frustration inside me must have been mutual between all of us. However, had I not seen her, I think my feelings of frustration would have been far greater.

Admittedly, I was shocked to see her on the 14th, not realising until then how poorly she was. And understandably she was fed up! However, as usual, we discovered ways of laughing and joking about the problems she had been dwelling on and, by Sunday, when I entered her room, I was greeted by the same cheerful Sarah I knew and loved. Her face was brighter, and we were soon giggling.

Sometimes, I wonder whether or not it is wrong...or silly... to get involved with other Cystics. We all know how serious the disease is, and, in a way, I suppose we risk getting hurt. But I don't for one minute regret our friendship, for we have given each other so much support these past two years.

In fact, she asked me why I had written to "That's Life" on her behalf and I said simply "Well. We have to support one another!" I think it hit us both then how much we have supported each other, and Sarah laughed and replied, " Yes!.. As always!"

I think that through living so far away from one another we have reassured each other in our thoughts. During the rough periods we knew that we were constantly encouraging each other to fight. Sometimes, whenever I feel fed up, I imagine what Sarah would say to me for feeling this way, and always I've ended up smiling!

As long as she is in my heart I shall keep on fighting for what she was also hoping for. And if I am lucky enough to receive a transplant, know that a little corner of my new heart is already reserved for her.

Please, try not to mourn her for too long, she wouldn't want that. She'll always be with you and, as she has proved to us all, it's better to "keep your chin up!"

I know you'll do your best to keep your own chins high because you are a wonderful family, and I know you must feel very, very proud of our dear Sarah.

With deepest sympathy,
Penny. xxx

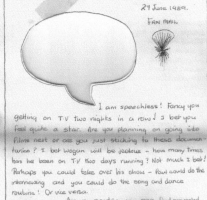

27 June 1989.

FAN MAIL

I am speechless! Fancy you getting on T.V two nights in a row! I bet you feel quite a star. Are you planning on going into films next or are you just sticking to these documentaries? I bet Wogan will be jealous - how many times has he been on T.V two days running? Not much I bet! Perhaps you could take over his show - Paul could do the interviewing and you could do the song and dance routine! Or vice versa.

Are you needing any more food smuggled in yet? I ask this as we have some left overs from Saturday night - not many, but a few. You should have seen the lads faces when they saw us in the saris. I think they wondered what they had come to. We ate the meal in the back room and by the time we'd finished the

dessert, Michele and Ian were well tipsy! They'd been drinking a Gin cocktail that Ian had brought - in fact they finished the bottle. I was on flat and boring alcohol-free Kaliber. It's not the most adventurous drink in the world is it! To finish with we had a liqueur - Creme de banana. I could have had a few of those, it was gummy.

We ended up playing cards later on. Talk about cheating! I've never seen such a dishonest bunch! It was fun though. Ian had some fake tan on too which we all teased. He'd put it on all unevenly and his hands looked horrible. I'll show you the photos we took, we got them back some time today, should be a laugh.

We are trying to raise yet more publicity. We can't think what to do next. I've altered my article slightly and I'm sending it to Readers Digest. I had considered writing to Wogan. How does Paul feel about appearing on that if we can manage to get through to him??? Hope it's not gone to his head this fame - is he still speaking to the likes of us I wonder? Has he recovered from the trip down there yet?

Dad has just set out for Bolton to pick up the photos, which reminds me I've had a large-ish photo done

19th June 89.

Dear Sarah,

I decided to scrap the letter I wrote and send this instead. Must say I don't recommend this brand !! Stick to neb pipes - you can't beat them.

I shall come over again one day this week so WATCH OUT !

Saturday should be good. Michele and I are planning an "Indian Evening" and have invited Ian and Andrew

along too! We're going to dress up in Saris which we are borrowing, and Indian music in the background. We're going to decorate the back room with an Indian theme and have Indian food. Should be fun! Even the invitations suggest they are going on a flight to an unknown destination. Should be a world tour, but it's hard enough just planning an Indian Theme. See you soon.

Chin Up
as always. Love from ×
×× Penny.

Keighley and Worth Valley Railway
Black Cat Cigarettes, just one of the period enamelled advertisements on view at Oakworth station.
Photo by R. Higgins

Printed by Colec-Parker Ltd, Royd Way, Keighley BD21 3LG

Published by the Keighley and Worth Valley Railway Preservation Society, Haworth, Keighley, West Yorkshire

WV147

Of Ian and, as his favourite place in our house is our freezer where all the ice cream is. I've stuck this photo onto the freezer door. He's sat with his arms folded looking really miffed so I've stuck a suitable caption onto the photo.

DON'T BLAME ME FOR EATING ALL THE ICE CREAM!!

He'll probably go mad when he sees it, but never mind.

However, as I am rapidly running out of news I shall not bore you any longer. I shall come and see you soon - I'm trying to avoid Dr Webb who is too keen to stick a ventilon in, so I MAY turn up in disguise.

(What lengths we go to eh!)

So, watch out for the stranger in dark glasses - could be me !

Lots of love,
Penny ×××

P.S. Big lick from Freeway. (ugh!) (Yuk!)

P.S. Mum's ladies at the group want to know if Paul will put them in his little black book! Whatever next! Perhaps he could just send copies of his autograph. Don't tell him though or he will be getting big headed!

You asked if I'd noticed all these Popping folk, who seem to be coming a new species and certainly on the increase. Yesterday for e.g. I was having a well earned rest (ha!) when -..POP... two of them appeared, and left me more exhausted – 1½ hrs later – than I was beforehand. On a Wednesday after church a lot of old ladies, who I once regarded as quiet and unobtrusive, have all suddenly turned into Poppers. And worse, they are heavily Perfumed Poppers (Sadists!) We have since had a defumer installed at the back door!

It's a device which detects Perfume Poppers and immediately pours water over them... Wicked eh! Aunty Margaret came a few weeks ago and she was wearing matching smelly stuff on her. Anyhow it was so strong we had to ask her to kindly go wash herself! (Embarassing or what) She was a bit fed up as she'd gone to the trouble of putting it all on, only to be told to go and remove it. It nearly killed me the fumes though. they were really strong. She came again on Bank Holiday Monday – at least she's still friends with us! – but I noticed she didn't have as much on that time.

Above: Letter relating to Auntie Margaret and her perfume.

Below: Penny's Auntie Margaret asked Penny to design a card for a party. Because Margaret was interested in sewing, Penny drew a zip!

Above: Sarah Justin with her mum and dad.

SEE IF YOU CAN FIND ALL THE FOOD I'VE
SMUGGLED IN FOR YOU! (Don't let on though)

Friday 9 June 1989.

NEWS IN BRIEFS ← (not original idea. Alas, copied!)

68 Church St.
HORWICH.

Hello!

It was great to receive your letter - very novel idea to write on loo paper - oh, you mean its actually writing paper?! Ooops. Well anyway, it was nice to hear from you anyway — cor, hows that for bad English. Two 'anyways!'

Nothing spectacular has occured here recently. I've finished reading 'Grey is the colour of hope' by Irina Ratushinskaya. Well worth a read if you're nothing to read at present. I loved it. The story was about a 28 yr old girl 'prisoned in a Soviet Labour Camp (the Author herself) in 1981 and how she survived the 7 yrs. (Reminded me a bit of Monsall with yukky food, hunger strikes, rooms that are either too hot or too cold. Etc. Despite similarities though Monsall is far more desirable. Yes, amazing though true.

Enclosed is a very interesting piece of garb - well, interesting I suppose to a 'feminist reader' like yourself. Mum took me into Bolton - rare occasion, a visit to be made the most of - and I zoomed into one of the best bookshops around for miles. (and miles and miles). I found a very interesting corner at the far end of the shop, sat on the carpeted floor, and BROWSED! It was wonderful. You may think it sounds odd - sitting on the floor! in a shop - but I assure you, no one cares and anyway they too are busy browsing so no-one really takes any notice. I bought an "Ellis Peters' book" - " City of Gold and Shadows" - now on pg. 26 Chpt 2. Seeing as I had some money saved — £30 to be exact - I was fair chuffed. I also bought "Walking Tall" by Simon Weston. This I have had a quick look at and it seems really interesting. Some of the photos are awful; I think it's amazing how they've patched him up - if thats the right word - so well.

We received a letter from Papworth this morning and inside was a cheque for the travelling expenses from 13 May. I'd forgotten we'd bothered to claim for that wasted trip. Needless to say Dad hurriedly put it in the bank before Mum saw it. WISE!

Michele has just rung from the new shop up Astley Bridge and says that although business is doing well, it's quieter this afternoon so "she thought she'd give me a ring'. I went up to the new shop for the 1st time last Friday. It's nice. Well set out and lots of room in the back part for preparing the food. I think her family are trying to fatten me up — must think I'm thin! — because the tea consisted of lots of fatty products. Somehow I managed most of it - though we had frying steak with it which was nice - but I had to leave the potatoe things which were covered in batter. Even Michele struggled eating those & she also left one.

I've bought Dad his fathers Day card - 19th isn't it? - and also san and Andrews birthday cards. Both on 21st June! Just my luck. Ians has a big yellow clown and looks like he did on Decembers Flag Day last year. Andrews has a cat peeping through a letterbox on it though it doesn't look like his 'Sherry'. As he is 20 this year I rubbed it in, which I can get away with as he's older than me. Oh, to be young! I asked him (in the card) if rheumatism, arthritis, blood pressure etc had set in yet, and said if he finds his eyesight failing, I would read the card to him! Then, to finish, I wrote "Happy Birthday Old Chap". (Hee Hee) Tell me, does maturity set in too when you reach 20? I hope not.

Well, I shall go and get back to my book. I hope you are recovering well, will visit soon and also write again before long. Sorry about the scrawl. Please forgive.

See you soon, but it would be nicer to hear that you are back home again.

Love for now,
Penny. - a young person of 19 blissful years!

PS: You got the postcode wrong too. BL6 6AB!

Usual address
Lancashire.
26 June 1989.

To, Sarah & Paul.

Hello! Well, I must say how Terrific "That's Life" was last night. You were both great - how long did it take you to 'prepare' for the camera men sarah? Hope you had a wash!

We all felt very proud of Paul, how did you keep so calm though? Friends have been ringing asking who the dishy filmstar was !!! (No, I don't think they meant Doc!)

Silly me burst into tears with relief that at least they had responded. I was glad they had transplanters on - Jo Beetles I met 14 days after her transplant last July. I write to her but I couldn't get over how well she looks now. In fact, she also went down to 5 stones - it's hard to believe. Well, you Two, well done. I'm really proud — let's hope it does some good.

See you soon! Love as always
to Mum, Dad, & Sam too. xxx Penny. xxx

PTO

Dear Beryl and Brian,
    You must feel very proud of Paul and Sarah, let's hope it does the trick, if you want any company anytime just give us a ring, or if you feel up to it ring anyhow to let us know how things are.
    Love to all Judith and John x

And last but not least.
To Sam
    Well Sam, sorry to hear you didn't get invited along to the studio with Paul but you would have probably been the star and stole the show. Maybe upstaged Paul. Better luck next time though, I think the secret is to play cricket. That way you meet the 'That's Life' team. Just don't start eating Esther's flowers if you get invited !!!
    Woof Woof
    from Freeway.

More news from the Opium Den.
"Neb House"
Misty Lane.
Coughinton Village.
Wheezex (or is that Wessex?)

Dear Sarah,

When your letter arrived I was still in bed and wondering why we were having a heatwave all night. It was awful. I couldn't breathe, couldn't sleep, couldn't get comfy. I'd tossed and turned all night, so I was a little bleary eyed whilst reading your letter to say the least! Thank goodness though I left my window open all night and that Dad turned off the heating for once.

I still haven't recovered from my holiday at — oh, what's it called? — er Papton I think. Oh no, Papworth. You've probably not heard of it, its only a small village. Hardly on the map even. Anyhow if you ever go there, don't stop — just keep driving!

Note the Green paper! I've only just noticed myself, but no doubt this will v. much appeal to a person of your — er — refined — taste. This shade is the very latest — known as the ever popular Pea Green. I don't think I have any green envelopes though but I've just had an idea. I shall send your letter in a sheet of this paper. I'll have to disguise its A4 Shape into an envelope —

Hey There's that place Penny mentioned. Lets call for a Doner kebab!

PAPWORTH

(unleaded of course)

'yo!'

① A4 Paper

② Glue.

③ Address & Stamp

Perhaps I should have used green ink too!

You asked if I'd noticed all these 'popping folk' who seem to becoming a new species & certainly on the increase. Yesterday for eg. I was having a well earned rest (ha!) when — POP — Two of them appeared, and left me more exhausted — 1½ hr later — than I was beforehand. On a Wednesday after church a lot of old ladies, who I once regarded as quiet & unobtrusive, have all suddenly turned into Poppers. And worse — they are heavily perfumed Poppers. (Sadists!) We have since had a dejuner installed at the back door! Its a device which detects Perfume Poppers & immediately pours water over them. Wicked eh! Aunty Margaret came a few weeks ago wearing matching smelly stuff on her. Anyhow it was so strong we had to ask her kindly to go wash herself. (embarrassing or what) She was a bit fed up as she'd gone to the trouble of putting it all on, only to be told to go & remove it. The fumes nearly killed me. She came again on bank Holiday Monday — at least she's still friends with us — but I noticed she didn't have as much on that time.

Heaven Sent, Taylor Made

Sarah passed away a day or two after the 'transplant' episode of 'That's Life' was aired. She died as a result of Cystic Fibrosis. It was expected, but tragic. Her coffin was laid out in the family's front room, and we went as a family to pay our respects. Sarah's passing hit Penny hard as they had become very close.

For Sarah.
(My brave Pal.)

I recognize the sound instantly. It is the same, familiar faint whimper that has resounded off my own four walls so many times before. A primitive cry of self pity. A cry of weakness...A cry of fear. Yet I can do nothing but lie silently, as though my body is in sleep, whilst the gentle sob cracks, brittle as an egg, and oozes a deep erratic cry from her heart. It holds me motionless. It is a cry that plunges into the depths of the most stubborn heart and rips it wide open.

I want to step from my cold, impersonal hospital bed, and cross over to where she lies, sobbing. To hold her hand in mine and murmur reassurance and understanding. I am torn ruthlessly apart, for I know what she is feeling. The burning inside her lungs equals that of my own. The gurgling sounds, and short gasping breaths unite with mine. But I know also that this despairing cry releases the damned cruel frustration that swells alongside the crippled innards of our young bodies. These sobs are thrust forcibly from our souls. And when the self pity ebbs quietly into the night and joins with the distant muffled noises of the ward then, and only then, will our haunted bodies rest.

The ghost of illness treads silently, relentlessly, along the corridor. Pacing the dawn hours. But we are safe for now. Our bodies sleep, and our minds flee into the night. Escaping! A night of freedom! Dreams are released - dreams void of pain, allowing us to forget. Dreams that give way to hope and reason. Reason to fight. And, above all, reason to live.

The beautiful hours come upon us. And hope breathes and glows within the confines of our weakened bodies. We become strong! And pain is unable to reach us. These are the hours of glory, when the ghost looses sight of us. We hide, and run ahead of unpleasantness.

White petals were scattered around the small table in the dining room, no longer clinging to their mothes branch. These last few days had witnessed their seperation, as the petals had fallen towards the soft green carpet beneath them. Likewise, the mother tree from which they had been parted, silently wept white petals of grief upon the garden lawn, where Sam, the family retriever, lay shading himself from the midafternoon heat.

At 1·00 on that particular afternoon I, too, had been sat in the garden in the shade. Sam, along with my two friends, Andrew and Ian, had sat with me, and the shadowed movement of the trees had a mesmirizing effect on us all. How many times Sarah had also sat in that same chair, with Sam at her feet, perhaps on a similar afternoon?

I reminded myself that this was no ordinary afternoon, and indeed we were all painfully aware of the inevitability of the afternoons events'. The three cars were waiting at the front of the house to leave at 1·30; last minute preparations were busily in progress inside; and the numerous white boquets were carefully taken note of as the contributors names' were added to the growing list. But as it approached the time that we intended to leave for the church, I was still trying to come to terms with the reason we were here, in Macclesfield. And although I found it difficult to accept, I knew that shortly I was to witness the burial of my dear friend Sarah who, at 20 yrs old, was only three months older than myself. And, worse; she had died whilst struggling to fight an illness that Ive both shared - Cystic Fibrosis.

Then suddenly, a vast field stretches endlessly before us. A profound, turbulant river streaks horizontal in the distance, and flowers of every wild species shine breathtakingly above the perpetual green blades. And we see the daises — white with hope — scattering our path. Chain upon chain of them surrounds us but we see only the single flower. And, holding it high above our heads, we laugh, and say;

"We are not ready to push these up".

And laugh again.

But now I see that she has run on ahead! She is no longer at my side!

She moves through the white field, and crosses the river. There is no bridge — except the bridge of faith. And across it she walks with ease to the other side, waving triumphantly.

Now she is free!

Free of pain, and fears.

And the white flower returns to the rich soil to live again.

I am alone. And I know that I too must cross the white field.

But suddenly I cry: "I am not ready yet, to push a daisy".

And saddened, I walk away.

Heaven Sent, Taylor Made

28 August 1989.

To dear Sarah.

   I am missing you so much of late. It is, today, two months since you died and broke my heart. At first, the pain was numbed. I carried on in the same manner that is me. And I was oblivious to your absence.

   But now, suddenly, the shock of losing you is upon me. I feel you near me every day and though I know you are willing me to fight harder, I am finding it so difficult. Sometimes, I just want to cry. No. To howl. But, you must understand – I am unable to do so. I keep trying to cry but my lungs object furiously and bleed. Oh, you know how it is! Laughable isn't it! HA HA! So, instead, a well is swelling inside me. This is what's known as "bottling it up" I guess. But, believe me, I cry inside. The hurt is almost a physical pain, but there is no painkiller for this.

   God. I miss you!

   I read through your letters last night. That nearly tore me wide open but I had to laugh at our obvious understanding – our mutual joking nature which was so apparent.

   Dad ate a mango too yesterday. It reminded me so much of your last letters, in which you said

   "I thought mango was a face pack!"

   (Nice one!)

   I was crying as Dad ate the mango though. He never saw me, but I was. Inside. My soul yearned to talk and laugh with you so much.

   So, you see, I'm all screwed up. I'm not mad at you. In fact I admire you. I doubt you'll ever know just how much I admire you. I always have, because you are a true fighter. The first day I met you I thought to myself "Here's a girl who hasn't got long to live" and that unnerved me. I was unwilling at first to become involved. But then, sharing a room, it was inevitable we'd become friends. And now, I'm glad we did.

   You taught me all the rules. The rules to fight. I had the best tutor! Somedays though I wanted to say "Look Sarah. Why!? Why, are you fighting so hard?" It wore me out to watch you. Your inner strength was unique.

   I remember though when Andrew died, in that room. It scared us didn't it; to be so isolated in death, we thought. How awful! But somehow, we dismissed that it could happen to us.

   And then came Papworth. A place of hope. A place that gave us reason to cry "This is what we fight for!" And suddenly we knew why.

   You put up such a brave fight. You'd have thumped me for calling you 'brave' wouldn't you? But then, you would say – "this isn't bravery. I didn't ask to be in this position. Who _wants_ a transplant really!? Sooner live off my _own_ guts".

   We didn't ask to be ill. But we made the best of it. Encouraged each other; laughed together. What the hell!

   I just wish you were still here. I'm on my own now. No you. No Debbie. No Louise ....

   Just me and the last shred of hope that we breathed from; lived off. Relied upon!

   I'm not stupid though. I know the risks – maybe I'll be joining you! But, I somehow, can't imagine doing so just yet. I don't know where you are. (Nor do I wish to know!) I feel that you're somewhere. Watching. Waiting.

   But I'm fighting for us now. I'm stronger because I have more reason for doing so; going through with it! But I wish you were here with me - encouraging each other.

   "As always!" love you Sarah,

   Penny.

99

Stephen Thomas

Penny met Stephen Thomas at Monsall and they soon built up a strong friendship. He lived in Fleetwood with his family, and they would write to each other regularly. They met sometimes at the hospital and Stephen visited Penny at home at times too. They had the same sense of humour and both enjoyed writing and artwork.

Penny and Stephen at Penny's home. Sadly, Stephen died while Penny was having her transplant. A fellow CF sufferer, he, like Penny, was prone to infection. Penny was devastated that she didn't get to say goodbye.

When Stephen was in hospital, Penny went to visit and decided to wear a Kiss Me Quick hat and sunglasses, and to take in a bucket and spade, to make him feel less homesick for Fleetwood. He laughed and thought she was crackers! Dr Webb said 'What are you like?'

DEDICATORY
FOR
STEPHEN THOMAS.

There was no time
To say 'Goodbye',
No time for final tears.
Though you were always
there for me,
Throughout those dying years.
So when at last November came
To bring me life anew
I woke to find that life had died
So silently in you.
You crept away so suddenly—
As swiftly as we'd met.
But may we ever find we have
No reason to forget
The times when just a single smile,
Or words of reassurance led
To optimistic, happy thoughts
In those darkened days ahead.
Dear Stephen, in your place of rest
I pray you've witnessed peace.
And when I follow, may we meet
In lifes gentle release.

Penny Taylor.
24.5.90

Heaven Sent, Taylor Made

Dear Penny,

Hello! I have just finished re-writing from a textbook all the questions that I got wrong in my ceramics mock exam. The question paper was very hard you know - which come to around two-thirds of the exam, or to put it another way, eight sides of A4 paper, and so you can see after all that writing I needed a break which is why I haven't written to you yet, but I will soon... ... Oh and here it is, see, I said I would write to you. Now then what shall I say now that I have got the excuse about my delay out of the way. Actually I thought it was a very good excuse, now I could have said that I became marooned on the Fleetwood to Knott-end ferry and I was dying of starvation, so had to eat up all the writing paper, but I don't think you would have believed me. But seriously though, I have been working very hard. I would like to take this point to say thankyou for your letter. It looks as though you have put an awful lot of time into the drawings on the envelope; they look really good. Your letters make mine look awfully drab, and so to brighten them up I am going to draw a self portrait :—

And there it is. Impressed eh! I bet you can spot the likeness straight away. Actually I think I may have have made my self look a little old, and so I will have to draw another one in which I look a few years younger.

heres a self portrait of me when I was younger, notice the whispy hair. Heres one of me wearing a disguise

Here a picture of a complete stranger

This is a drawing of my house and family

All these drawings has reminded me that I went down to london about two weeks ago to look around some of the museums and galleries. We had to catch the 6-20 am train from Blackpool which went straight through to London. This meant that I had to wake up at the undreamt of time of five o'clock in the morning. I always remember to take plenty of things to drink with me on the train, because tea is always something like 55p just for a small carton. The funny thing was that on the return journey, most of the student were drunk and were singing and shouting, or falling asleep, and everyone was making a complete fool of themselves. It was a really good trip home. The museums in london are all free to enter, but there are big signes saying. "It costs one pound per second to run this museum. It is you choice if you want to make a contribution or not. The suggested amount, it says, is two pounds per person." So if you are a hard up student and cannot afford to pay, then you have to shamefully shuffle past at least five attendants at the pay desks who are waiting for you contribution, and when they dont get any, you can tell them staring at you as you go by. The underground is a great place to get lost in, even though the map of the routes are supposed to be easy to understand I did manage twice to get on the right train, but going in the wrong direction. It is a very interesting city to visit, but even the short time which we were there I started to feel very insignificant and insecure. It is such an unfriendly place where nobody seems to matter. You could drop dead on the pavement and people would just trample over the top of you. Thats the feeling that I got anyway. It is as though people are frightened of each other and nobody trusts anybody else. When I returned home Fleetwood seemed so small and quiet in comparison to the hustle and bustle of a big city, but thats the way I like it. People are much more friendly here. In your letter before last you said there is a signe above the doorway to the college, it says "All who enter here abandon all hope", or something similar, well thats funny that because we also have a signe above our doorway to college, it says something like... ... "entrance". ha! well maybe not. We have a similar one which says "exit". I was out with a few of my friends on Wednesday a few days ago and about 11'o'clockish they decided they wanted to go into Blackpool to a night club well I was wearing Jeans which meant the only place we could get into was a real dive and there was always trouble there. Anyway I couldn't afford to get in, so I went home. two of them decided to go and one of them 'Mark' picked his car up from home and drove down there They told me that at 2 o'clock they came out and Mark tried to drive home but he was really drunk because he had been drinking since nine Apparently he was approaching some traffi' lights on the wrong side of the road and hit a police car. What a night, and I missed it. I'll say goodby to you now before I run out of page, and also to leave myself some things to say in my next letter.

bye. love steve.

Just one example of the vast library of communications between Penny and Stephen from Fleetwood.

Dear Penny

I managed to escape eventually from Monsall vowing never to go there again. What a drag it was though going in for a second time so soon after the first. It probably serves me right for mentioning that I happened to have a pain in my chest. Now when the Doctor askes me how I am I say "fine or great or couldn't feel better". Its been my birthday since you wrote to me last and now I'm a grand old 18 year old. I must have said weeks and weeks beforehand "Don't buy any cards because they're a waste of money, and then come the day and the T.V set is full of "Happy Birthday" cards again.

Its been a very busy time for me just recently because all the polys are having there open days and we're all having to decide which ones to visit. A couple of weeks ago a few of us went to look around Manchester poly. Its suposed to have a really good reputation and is quite hard to get into but having seen round the place I now have other ideas about it. We went into four carparks which were all full. At one of them I stoped at the barrier waiting to be let in by the attending attendant. We was waiting for about a minute when he said "Yes". Erm "can I come in and park please". "Not in here mate". He said, I mean what a stupid question to ask someone entering a car park in a car. I should have asked him if I could swap it for a better one. In the fine art department the sculpture was so bad that it was hard to tell if we were looking at just junk or somebodies actual work. By about 2 o'clock I was really hungry because I hadnt had anything to eat (obviously a good reason to be hungry) so I said probably for the eleventh time, "how about something to eat now. We were right in China town and so I suggested a chinese but after looking at the price list they said no! Chicken curry and rice was about £2.80 to eat in which I thought was quite reasonable. I said "look over there, a McDonalds", but they wouldn't go in. Julie said lets go into the Pizza hut down the road they're cheap. It wasn't until we sat down and started looking at the menu that we found out she was wrong. We had to wait ages to be served. I didn't know wether to click my fingers and say waiter, but was afraid that I may get spagetti bolognase tipped over my head which is what I ordered. The two girls where looking at all the fellers and saying things like "oh he's nice and look at him". I think its terrable that folk should carry on like that.

Manchester is such a hard place to drive around if you don't know where you are going. Julie was supposed to be reading the map but she didn't know her left from right and kept saying this one, no, next one, or is it the one we've just passed. Up here no down there. Where abouts are we now then? Needless to say that we got lost a few times.

A week after that I went to Hull by train. I wasn't sure wether or not it was quite a good idea because there has been alot of train crashes recently. I didn't like one bit where we went over the Pennines and went through a tunnel which must have been over two miles long because it took ages to get through and I was wondering what would happen if the train was to stop there and we all had to walk back out again. Can you imagine what it was like for those who built the tunel. All I could see out of the window was blackness.

I had to change trains at Manchester and the second train went through Miles platting and I could just make out Monsal next to the Wilsons brewery. I was glad we were just passing. The scenery going through Yorkshire was really nice. Leeds was not at all like I expected it to be. It seemed quite a pleasant place with old gothic buildings and narrow shopping streets. It's quite amazing what you can see from out of a train window, but why do I always seem to get on a train that squeeks or I pick a seat where the head restraint is missing or the cushion keeps falling off. We went under the Humber bridge Wow! its so big its really undescribable. its bigger, for instance than this and thats really saying something!! Hull, it seemed to me was a very clean city everything was fresh and new even though most of the architecture was several hundred years old. The Poly was situated at the end of a park which had fountains everywhere. The college itself looked like a spanish four star hotel. People there don't half talk funny though, even funnier than you do. It was so windy that day though it was untrue. I took a look down at the ten quayside and could hardly stand up straight. It was much windier than Fleetwood ever gets. It was so cold aswell that my hands were turning blue so I had to go into a pub. Well, you know how it is. Anyway the pub was about the size of a shoe box and was absolutely packed with drunkard sailors swaying around everywhere. There was a hangmans noose hanging from the ceiling. I thought what a rum place this is.

On the train coming home there was an obstruction on the track in front of us.

(5)

and we had to crawl along at 20mph. Luckily I didn't miss the train at Manchester which I caught at half nine at night and got me into Blackpool for quarter to eleven. The journey took four hours there and four back, enough to say I was shattered by the time I got to bed.

Last weekend I went out to look for a new car, well newer car with my brother. We looked at one, a Fiat 126. I wasn't sure what one was, but I do know now, they're so small they make minis look like limosines not really the kind of vehicle for an up and coming young executive. I had a meaner looking pedal car when I was seven. In the end I got a nice white Honda accord. Its really smooth and quiet, not like my last one where I had to turn the radio full on th to drown the sound of the rattles. My new cars has fifth gear too so I'm a real boy racer in my dark glasses and leather gloves. I haven't aquired a furry dice yet though. Patch keeps asking me if I would start giving him driving lessons, but I'm not too sure about that because last time I let him behind the wheel he took off after a cat.

Last Thursday I used it to drive down to stoke. It was really bad on the motorway

(6)

it was raining so hard and with the spray from the lorries I could hardly see where I was going and was glad to be off the Motorway. I thought North Staffs poly was probably the best I had been to and will probably put that as first choice. Accomodation there is also very good rent on average is around £14. if sharing a house with two other people. You ought to see the houses though, they look like something off Coronation street I can't wait to be living away from home, somewhere different. It will probably take some getting used to but I think I need a change after living at home for 25 years. I don't fancy having to do all my own washing though, and think of all that cooking I will have to do for myself I'll probably end up burning something, hopefully not the house. Anyway it is possible to get put in the halls of residence where all meals light and heating is provided for.

When I got my car I went around to show it to my mate and he came hobbling out like an old man because apparantly he had been for a night in Preston the night before and had gotten a train back to poulton for 11.30 unfortunatly no buses were running so he decided to walk it the four miles home. Deciding to make a shortcut he ran down the embankment onto a disused track and follow it into Fleetwood but as he was running down the embankment he hit a stake that was sticking up and went tumbling into a bush of thorns

(7)

which took him 20 minutes to escape from, so by the time he walked it home for 2.00 o'clock in the morning all his pants and leather jacket where torn. While I was at his house he taped a few albums for me one of which I am listening to at the moment, Thomas Dolby. Its one of the best tapes I've ever heard. Patch likes listening to Def Leppard at 6'oclock in the morning and wakes me up. When I go down stairs and find him head banging in his leather bike jacket

Sometimes he cruises down to the greasy hand with his girlfriend where all the mad Dogs hang out and pretends to be really mean and moody.

Summers coming now at last, you might not know what summer is, its that time when the sun is out and its not raining but living in Horwich I think for you thats a rare occasion, never mind I'll draw you a diagram of what to expect. All the people of Horwich say "what on earth is that bright light in the sky. Anyway I'm ready for a bit of sunshine again. Although it doesn't seem so long ago since christmas, last summer seems long distant and I've forgotten what it feels like to be warm.

After reading the poem you wrote in your last letter I thought about writing one back although I don't think that I haven't written one before so here goes. I'll make this one up as I go along.

(8)

I once knew a girl called Penny,
There was only one of her, there weren't many.
She lived in a town called Horwich,
Some say she was a witch
but all though I don't know her all too well
I know she could never cast a spell
because although she thinks that she's quite smart
I've seen more sence in a donkeys smile.

Well perhaps you've got competition now this may go down as one of the great writings in English history by the way I did think your drawing of a smiths crisp looks nothing like a pebble. I know these things of course being a pebbleologist we in the trade also call ourselves stonists. The poem about the stone was very nice (not as good as mine of course) but what does it mean. I think my pens beginning to run out again so I must go now. I won't read the letter through but leave it to you to find the mistakes so I'll send it as I have written it.

see you.

love
steve

Wednesday.

DATE :- August 1988 - Late at night when everything is quiet and folk can concentrate on letter writing. As usual it's raining outside.

Survival tips from the Monsall grapevine

Hello Stephen.

Now you know why so many Monsall patients recieve grapes from their visitors! Of course I couldn't very well send you the real thing because by the time they'd have arrived you would have ended up with soggy purple writing paper.

Just what the Dr ordered - A bunch of Grapes!

What to do with grapes :-

① Squash to a pulp. Don't forget to wash feet first!

It's very difficult knowing just what to send to a person whilst they're staying in the holiday camp of the North. I could have sent you a map explaining where the secret passage and escape route is in Ward 15 but as yet I haven't found it myself so that would have been no good. I could have sent you a 30 ft piece of rope so you could escape via the window but what's the use of that in a ground floor building?!

② Collect juice

Maybe a torch would have been ok so that you could find your way along the dark corridor at night to the main entrance. Or perhaps a train ticket for Fleetwood would have been more appropriate. However I'm afraid you'll have to do without because I didn't think of this until I'd sent you the letter. Ha! (That's a lie of course because I would have written it in the letter otherwise would I). Still, I suppose you'll get by sketching the lovely grounds that surround you. You could paint the many varieties of rare flowers, do pen and ink sketches of the exquisite fountains that are displayed on the carefully tendered lawns, and do quick pencil drawings of the sound architecture on those wonderful old buildings. There's just no end to the number of things to do and see at Monsall, no wonder you like to stay there. Personally however I prefer home comforts.

③ Inject juice into drip bag.

④ Use four times a day, or when required.

I hope they remember to feed you down at the bottom end of the 'chalet'. A person could get forgotten down there. Maybe the ghost keeps you company. He usually creeps in during the small hours rattling his chains (he lost the key), strolls down the corridor towards the kitchen where the nurses are snoozing, raids the biscuit tin then runs back down to your room where he then watches 24 hr telly. So watch out if you've got crumbs in your bed!

I was quite surprised to see 3 Stephens in the ward at the minute. Could this be a record? And they'd put you all down the same end. How is the 'iron pumping' going? Are they putting you all through the tough training schedule or do they just think you need a few extra muscles? I bet you wish you'd joined the Army instead for 2 weeks, it could be easier.

My first thought when I started to write this letter was to invent the first small piece of A4 paper and introduce big writing. However my next thought was that long letters probably help to pass a few minutes — no doubt you've got a good few minutes to spare! So I got scribbling with my favourite pen then, when it was finished, I put on my walking boots (which I first broke in by clobbering them a number of times with a big hammer!!) then walked a long way up a big hill to the Pigeon tower to post my letter. However, all the Pigeons were flying up to the Glasgow Garden Festival that day so I had to make do with a tiny, frilly edged piece of paper called a stamp. Hope it's as reliable as the birdies! On the way home I bumped into Bugs Bunny eating a large carrot. He said "whats up Doc?" so I told him how I was wanting to get this terribly urgent letter to you. He finished munching away at his oversized carrot and said if it wasn't for the fact that his two chompers had a dental appointment he would have delivered it. However I said it was OK and that I understood and besides you can't always rely on "hare-mail" these days, so I said Goodbye to him and came home.

Did you know that before we had hare-mail, horses used to deliver it instead? Remember old Pegasus, the legendary flying horse? Anyhow here's a little rhyme about how the hare-mail came about ~

Naigh! A Flying rabbit! Whatever next?

① I once knew a horse
His name was Gus
He delivered all the post
Without any fuss.

② And then one day
A bunny hopped by,
Grabbed old Gus's mail bag,
And started to fly.

③ He delivered all the letters,
With the greatest of ease.
Yet all the locals laughed
At this bun above the trees.

④ There's a moral in this story
And a point to this tale.
Never take for granted
Our good old hare-mail.

Well. I've been writing this letter now for about an hour and I still haven't got round to telling you about all these exciting things that have been happening lately. The other night I went up to Lesleys for a gab. She has this aggravating little brother that interrupts the conversation every 5 minutes so we spent most of the time thinking of ways to avoid him. The rest of the time we

talked about her favourite place - Henri Africas - where (as she calls them) all the 'funny folk' go. She's got about 60 photographs of the place and now knows all the folk who work there really well. It's amazing how convincing the blokes look when they've got their high heels and glam on. With some of them you have to really look at them to tell whether or not they are men. It's a weird place. Anyhow, when we'd finished going through the photos we started winding up this singing clown she has and having a laugh at it. Its head sort of goes round as its singing. Anyhow about ½ hr later it suddenly started to sing again without either of us winding it up. It was really spooky, then when it stopped it just seemed to sit staring at us both. I doubt Lesley slept that night in case it come to life.

This week I've been busy trying to recall certain dates relating to hospital visits, being transferred to Monsall etc. You see, the Papworth gang said I'm the first cystic to go there that enjoys writing so they've asked me to try and write an account of all that's been going on since a transplant was suggested so that other patients will realise that it's the same proceedure for all the patients. Well, I may as well try and attempt to have a go at it. It's not easy though as I haven't a clue where to start. There's a mound of information but it's difficult knowing which piece to dig out first.

I've already designed some cards for patients recovering from the op. The message on the card suggests that they are making good progress. What I'm intending to do is to get some printed, send them down there and ask them if they'd like to sell them in order to raise some money for the Transplant foundation. They keep saying that money raising ideas are welcome and this is the only thing I could come up with at present. I'll send you one after my op. and let you cast a critical eye over it.

Freeway's sat here with me at the moment. Earlier he made me jump as a spider tried to climb up his whisker so he snapped at it. Meanwhile I was busily writing away so his sharp movement startled me. We seem to be overrun by budding incy-wincys at the moment — one decided to take a shower with me the other day and gave me the fright of my life. Anyway, it drowned in the water that had filled up in the shower basin and so I made sure it went rapidly down the plughole. Then, on Sunday, I went to church with Gran and we ended up sitting right at the back where all the spiders like to live. You only need to look at the floorboards and you can see the cobwebs. Yuk! Gran reckons spiders are lucky so our house should be the luckiest house in Horwich.

I'm going now. Freeway asked me to give him a mention so here he is → Let me know if you survive the whole 2 wks, we don't want two ghosts rattling their chains!!

Freeway doing his owl impression.

Love for now.
Penny. X

Oh, I do like to be beside the seaside...

P.S. Went for this amazing meal last night with Micheles family. Did you know that one glass of Asti and a wee bit of Creme de Menthe can make you squiffy? No, I didn't know either but I soon found out! The meal was great — pork, bamboo shoots, walnuts, bean shoots, potatoes - Yum! They took us to this really posh place, fancy decor, soft lighting, the lot. Glad I didn't turn up in an old pair of Jeans and Jumper!!

You can tell my hand got tired by the time I'd finished the letter.

BYE.

Dear Penny,

I always find the hardest part of a letter is actually starting it, which is why in this case I have started it by telling you how hard it is. This doesn't sound very sensible does it. That's because it isn't. Anyway at the moment I have just returned from doing some christmas shopping, or I was supposed to. I went down to Blackpool with the good intention of buying something for my sister whos fifteen and maybe even my two brothers. and of course my twin brother patch who said he wanted a home brew kit. When I went through the shops looking at all the games and different things I didn't have a clue what to buy. so I didn't buy anything. The shops were packed and it took ages to get down the small passageways (I was going to say "Isles" but can't spell it) Lewiss is good because you can spend all day riding up and down the escalators. The best shop I went in though was Beatties toy and model shop. It has a miniture railway in the window and the shop is full of toy cars and "Transformers", but I couldn't really get my sister one of those. so eventually when I got back home I just gave her some money to buy some shoes. I'm such a defeatist aren't I.

I was trying to do my christmas shopping a little earlier this year instead of leaving it all to christmas eve. which is what I usually do and then it's a big panic rushing around everywhere and usually buying things that nobody really wanted. but they usually say "ah er yes well thankyou, how did you know I've been wanting a set of handkerchiefs." I always get a really cheapy bottle of aftershave bought me every christmas usually "Hi karate" which is about 80p a pint. Sometimes if I have a feeling that I know what it is. I wrap it up again quickly and put it in patches stocking

College broke up a few days ago on friday. we went in at the same time in the morning and tidied up all our work areas. Some people had brought in bottles of wine and were already well drunk by about 11 oclock. Anyway we worked till about twelve then went down to Rankes hall which is a pub if you can't guess where. upon I proceeded to get very sloshed I hadn't had any dinner which made me feel even more drunk. luckily I didn't do anything stupid. Err I don't think. There were some girls with a water pistol, squirting people in the gents toilets I got completly covered with sensible string and silly foam. I Thought we were all very drunk until I saw the tutors wobbling about from side to side. They weren't setting a very good example. Patch was sick in the toilets. He goes anywhere where thers drink. but doesent put his paws in his pocket all that often.

When the Rankes closed a 3.30 we all went down the road to "stanley arms" until five oclock whereupon I got the bus home.

Do you know that I actually started to write this letter about 2 weeks ago and then I re-wrote it and re-wrote it so I hope it gets to you before christmas.

My friend moved up to Fleetwood to live about four weeks ago. He used to live in Blackpool but didn't like it because of the noise and the type of people that live there. When I used to go and visit him it usually meant me staying over at his flat which was quite awkward sometimes especially if I was at college the next morning but now he just lives at the other side of the park which is about a ten minuet walk. The problem now is that I probably wont be going for any more nights out in Blackpool which used to be a change from staying in Fleetwood all the time.

Well time in certainly flying by and it probably won't be long before I am moving out of Fleetwood myself. I am really looking forward to going somewhere and not living with my mum and dad anymore and having to listen to their arguement. but I think I will miss my dog and also probably miss just local things like streets and shops and the sound of boats in the distance. I don't think I'll miss the trams though.

I haven't been to any Rachmaninov concerts recently -yawn- Our idea of the arts around here is a night out at the flicks followed by a fish and chip supper. you are very sofisticated if you eat them with one of those plastic forks. Actually I was at the pictures last monday. when we have a free period. There was a film by George Lucas He did the star wars films and so we thought the special effects must be good. The film was called "Willo" and it was about this dwarf who finds a special baby whos really a princess and will grow up to rule the country and the wicked witch wants all babies killed at birth so that she can dominate the land and the story is about this dwarf protecting the baby from her. Its a bit like Sinbad films. You will probably enjoy it if you haven't seen it already. It will probably reach Horwich cinema in about 1994.

A TYPICAL HORWICH CINEMA.

Why are packets of sweets so monsterous in cinemas. It imposible to buy normal size bars of chocolates and things. Even tubes of smarties are about six metres long (slight exaggeration) A bag of popcorn takes about an hour or more to eat and thats only if you offer them to everyone in the cinema. About 3 people. Patch gets on my nerves when I go with him because he smokes and allways blows it in my direction. Doesn't it seem really peculier peculier funny after being inside a cinema in the afternoon where it is really dark and then walking out into the daylight. I always think its going to be nighttime outside.

I'll tell you what I am getting for christmas then: An old fashioned style pocket watch with a skeleton case so that the moving parts can be seen working. My sisters getting a thing shaped like a guitar but its not a guitar. Its something els that you play like a peano, but its not a piano and can sound like any musical instruments you want it to. It also has different beats in its memory to play along to and the beats can be changed into various styles such as raggae. Jazz Folk. Boogie Woogie - whatever that is - blue grass. It even made me sound competant when I tried to play it must be magic! Patch just sang along and did a soft paw shuffle.

Its a definate signe winter is here when the birds start sticking their beaks into the milk and pinching it. We had a bird in the garden the other day which was green and yellow with a light blue head. I am not sure what kind it was because my knowledge of birds is not all that good, but at a guess I could say it was an ostrich or perhaps one of those yellow, green, blue heads that you hear so nothing about.

Well I don't think that I'll be having much of a christmas "holiday" as I have practicly tons and tons of work to do. They're a mean old lot here. I think most of the tutors should be visited by the 3 ghosts of christmas to make them a bit more jolly. I should be getting three weeks off really but I go into Monsall on the 2nd of January which means I'll be in Manchester for the sales which may come in handy as I need some new clothes anyway. I hope Patch doesn't come visiting like he did last time all he does is eat up my crisps and drinks my lucozade switches the television station over then watches some boring documentery for the rest of the night until its time to go then borrows the train fare home and enough to get himself a beer on the way to the station. He's a right con merchant.

When I was going around the shops today I found lots of things that I wanted, but they're all for ages between 5 to 10. do you think this could probably suggest something about me. I would like to say thankyou for your carol and present. Whatever it is - I havent opened it yet (then) I hope you have a great time this christmas. Make sure youre dad doesn't get drunk with the vicar again

lots of love
steve.

27th July 88

Dear Stephen,

GREAT NEWS! I'm on the list at Papworth. We had the most exhausting time whilst we were down there as we were watched all the time to see how we coped with all the shocks and surprises they had in store for us. NOTHING was disguised about the op. - they told us everything, showed us around intensive care, described all the tubes and wires you have in you when you come round, told us all the nasty bits, ETC. Now, if youre not put off by all that then youre either daft, or keen!! (Yes, you're right, I'm daft!) What do you think of the newspaper article? Meet Freeway!! I bet you didn't really believe I had a dog called Freeway did you. Well, he's cute isn't he. The article was on page 3 of our local rag ~ I'm probably the first page 3 girl to have her clothes on! Note the Lowry jumper, very arty isn't it.

Lowry impression → of Freeway.

The photographer came last friday and it was his idea to have Freeway on the photo. Anyhow, as soon as he suggested this, Freeway ran up to me, sat up and looked at the camera. The chap said "he's done this before hasn't he!" You can tell he's a poser by the photo can't you.

I've just completed yet another course of I.V treatment, it gets rather tedious after a few days. Still, they let me do the whole course at home again and the venflom lasted two weeks so it was much more pleasant than last time. Now I'm feeling quite healthy once more. The only problem is that I've had to hold my wrist in such a funny position that I'm now finding it difficult to bend it again. Ever felt silly?

Last Tuesday I met the world famous, mega channel four super stars of ---- Treasure Hunt! We just happened to stumble across their secret base in the depths of an open field at The Last Drop Village. (Yes, I thought you'd know it well.) We just happened to spot the helicopter plus crew and pilot landing and thought "ah! there's Treasure Hunt". So we took a photo, had a chat then went in search of our car. We followed the clues, paused for a couple of adverts, then found it at the corner of the field. We had thought if the bleeper went off we would ask the "T.H" crew for a lift to Papworth - I wonder if they would have obliged?

What are you planning to do now you've left collage? Tour the Globe? Become a famous artist? Eat fish and chips? Just think of all the exciting things you could do! You could even become a chief cleaner at Monsall (if you're really desperate).

Well. I'm going to go and watch TV now. Not that theres anything interesting on. "Vietnam" is on tonight, I might watch that. Its not bad.

Write soon.
Love Penny.

Andrew Burton

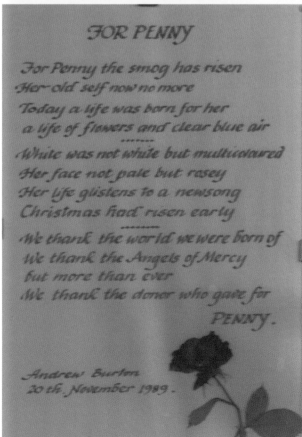

FOR PENNY

For Penny the smog has risen
Her old self now no more
Today a life was born for her
a life of flowers and clear blue air

White was not white but multicoloured
Her face not pale but rosey
Her life glistens to a newsong
Christmas had risen early

We thank the world we were born of
We thank the Angels of Mercy
but more than ever
We thank the donor who gave for
PENNY.

Andrew Burton
20th November 1989.

Andrew Burton was a fellow CF sufferer. Penny met him at Papworth and he was very supportive of her and the others. He was an architect and he and his wife were always there for Penny and for us, even offering us accommodation when we had nowhere to stay. Andrew didn't get his transplant until months after Penny had received hers, but sadly he didn't live long after this—he was actually the 100th CF transplant at Papworth. Jean (also pictured above) used to be the Secretary of the CF Trust in Bolton, and lost her son, Christopher. They moved to an area near

Papworth and it was where she was living there that she heard about Penny. She visited her near enough every day and was a wonderful support.

My friend Andrew.

The day you left us all wet eyed
And ruddy cheeked, for we had cried,
I felt you had not left at all
But merely stepped from lounge to hall.
And in that passage you stood and watched
And thought it sad that we should cry.
But understand we are niave,
Indeed ourselves know not yet why.
Maybe we will never know completely why you left,
Until we too are stood with you —
                    And others stand bereft.
But what I feel and know so true
Is you're no longer 'breathless you'.
Your spirit is not restricted there
For in the passage is pure fresh air.
Perhaps your work here was complete
And so you stepped into the hall ?
Maybe the view looked nicer there ?
Or maybe you heard the faintest call ?
A call which urged you through the door and on ~
Across the hall you have now gone ~
There's someone there who most needs you
In Heavens playroom —
                    You and Drew.

                    Penny Taylor.
                    4th March '91.

Steve Sparkes

When Penny was recovering from her transplant, Steve came to Papworth, needing a heart and lung transplant. They got friendly and our family even went to stay with Steve's family in Wales.

Monday 15th July 1991

Dear Penny,

        Hiya Kiddo ! I hope that you are OK and you don't have an infection what a pain, but yet, you manage to keep cheerful. It amazes me actually how you are so bubbly all the time. Tineke was like that when I first met her, but now have managed to slow her down to my level !!

    I too, had a good time when you were here, even if it was a little tiring (Ok a lot tiring then !!) It was a break for me to ease the monotomy (I can't spell) of my life at present. Meeting you again after such a long time was good, you can never have too many friends, If only more people were like you and had your attitude this planet would be a better place to live. As you saw, all of my friends are fit and I don't get much chance to be myself either, but they are very nice people and I spend my time telling them that I am going to be OK !! Actually I thought maybe you thought I was ignoring you a bit when we went to the pub, I do tend to get carried away when I haven't seen them for such a long time.

    At the moment I do not feel to good, I have been working on my poems and putting this book together, I spent all day saturday and sunday on it and still haven't finished it, I also have this maths course I want to finish, in two weeks, before Tineke comes down again. Hopefully I should have enough time but last night I collapsed into bed at 9.30 and I didn't wake up till 10 am, so perhaps I am pushing my luck a bit !!!

    Thanks for the photos, actually I didn't realise I looked so ill !! God, I was quite shocked. (I'm a ugly spud anyway !) I still have some film left in my camera, but when I get it developed I will send you some copies of the ones I took, and some more flattering pics of me !!

    My Great Aunt was here yesterday, and I showed her the photos, she says she hasn't got any recent ones of me (The last one was when I was 8.) she would like a copy of the one with me and the triffid, the one with the plant growing out of my head, yes, she is strange my Auntie, anyway I will cover the cost if you could possibly get another done ?

    No other news really, write soon and I hope your Ok for transplant games Anytime you want to come down again just give me a ring. Take care,

love
Steve
xxxx

Andrew David Morley

Top to bottom. Andrew Morley relaxing, juggling and spending time with his mum.

Andrew came to visit Penny from his teenage years as they'd met one another at school. He spent a lot of time at our house, playing board games, cards, Monopoly, Contraband and many others. He loved riding his bike and soon discovered that we also had pushbikes. Soon we all went together to cycle trails and to Fleetwood.

Penny loved to go out for meals and would go to places like the Italian Orchard in Preston, or Anna's at Darwen. They often went out as a group with Thomas and Michele, Michael and his friend, Mark Burgess and Julia.

By this time Penny was losing her mobility and she couldn't do the things she had been able to before, but Andrew would not let that stop her and he took her to places like Manchester. He would put her on his back and carry her around the shops. He even carried her up Rivington Pike and back one day!

Andrew soon came everywhere with us. He would come to relations at Christmas and to lots of our friends' homes. He came on holidays to Belmont, the Lake District and many other places. He liked to use his video camera and one year he produced a video of Rivington, including the school which both he and Penny had attended. He also made a video of local people for John's friend, Ken Ward, in New Zealand.

During Cystic Fibrosis week we held a fundraising event and John made some clown outfits. He and Andrew spent their days in Bolton raising money in their costumes.

Over many years Andrew attended Monsall Hospital with Penny. One night he was on his way to watch a video we had hired, but in the matter of seventeen minutes (the time it took him to cycle from his home in Adlington to our house in Horwich) everything changed.

Penny had taken a turn for the worse and needed to be taken urgently to the hospital. So, Andrew put his bike in our cellar and came with us to the hospital. The ward at Monsall was quiet as, it being the weekend, most patients had gone home. Because of this, Penny (being Penny) asked if Andrew could stay for the night, and he did so in an unoccupied room. Penny was very fortunate in that quite a lot of her friends would visit her in hospital: Michele and Thomas, Michael and many other friends.

Penny's health was deteriorating more and more, and when she was eighteen years of age Dr Webb told her she should consider going down the transplant road, which she eventually did.

In 1989 Penny got her transplant and for two years had a

Andrew and Penny at Papworth.

Above: Andrew, Penny and Robin (cousin Roy's son) with Harvey the dog during a Transplant Games visit.

new life. Andrew was a massive part of that new life. One of our most memorable holidays with Andrew was in Derbyshire. We had a wonderful couple of weeks out on our bikes cycling the Tissington trail at the time of the well dressings. Penny and Andrew went down the Blue John Mine and we all went on the cable car at Matlock Bath. We had lots of fun and lots of laughs, and it turned out to be our last holiday all together.

But, in September, Penny entered the Transplant Games in Glasgow and we stayed with Judith's cousin Roy, his wife Anne, and their children, Veronica and Robin, in Kelvinside in Glasgow. Of course, Andrew came with us to the Games and stayed at Roy and Anne's with us. But, after the games, Penny was not well and we all went down to Papworth Hospital where it was found that Penny was losing her new lungs and was therefore coming to the end of her life.

We all stayed with Reverend Paul and Anita Duffett for what we at first thought would be a short stay, but it turned out to be three weeks. Paul and Anita were wonderful. They made us so welcome and gave us the full use of their house for the time we were there. Andrew was a true friend and later that year he got engaged to Penny before she died. Our Vicar, Denis Gatenby, held an engagement service for them out of an old prayer book which his wife, Dorothy, found. Even after Penny died, Andrew continued to attend church with us for many years. He was very precious to us, but suddenly passed away on 3rd November 2018. He will never be forgotten.

Above: Penny, Veronica and Andrew staying at Roy and Anne's house during the Transplant Games.

Andrew and Penny during their final Christmas together.

Andrew and Penny at Penny's home. They spent a lot of time together and Andrew was so supportive of her, through good times and bad.

Andrew fundraising.

Andrew performing at a tribute concert.

Andrew at Papworth with Goodforhugs—a teddy given to Penny by Sharon. Penny gifted Goodforhugs to Andrew when she knew she was dying.

Sharon, who gave Penny Goodforhugs, the teddy, and had been a good friend of Penny's for many years.

Above: Penny with Andrew at Manchester Cathedral for the ordination of their friend Jonathan who also features as an illustration in Penny's poem above right.

'BEDTIME' BLUES

Hello   . I've time on my hands!
I'm tucked up in bed with no cares or demands.
The Doctor, he's told me to 'sit down and rest'
If I want to avoid a bad pain in my chest.
The problem, it started on Sunday at eight-
I couldn't get up, as I went to bed late!
But I had to get going, for at ten we were due
At Manchester Cathedral, in time for a pew.
So I dashed round the house and gulped down my food-
Half was uneaten, and half was unchewed-
But by quarter past nine we were all on our way
And much looking forward to the rest of the day.
We arrived in good time- a few minutes we'd gained-
All set to watch Jonathan being ordained.
Whilst walking along, we met him arriving-
He was happy and beaming, though glad not to be driving!
This was to be a big day in his life
And we would all witness, along with his wife,
The service in which this young man would cease
To be deacon; for now we could call him a priest.
So the service began, and we sat at the front!-
Yes, we could see everything, from Altar to Font-
And gleaming and sparkling the Bishop walked in,
Followed by a line of his holy men.
All were dressed up, in gold, white and red,
Clutching their Bibles and bowing their head.
The sight was stupendous and held us in awe-
Then prayers soon followed, according to Gods Holy Law.
And then we were singing, a tune bright and gay,
But suddenly a problem came clouding my day:
I'd sung the first verse, for the second I waited,
When...boom, boom, boom,... my heart palpitated!
It gave me a panic, I sat down real quick,
Though not knowing what to do made me feel quite sick.
With luck it subsided, and beat back to norm,
By then I felt tired, and a little forlorn.
The service, it finished, some time around noon
And by one we were home. I went up to my room.
All afternoon though, I felt bright and breezy-
No sign of a cough. And I didn't feel wheezy.
So, at 6.22, I decided to go
To church (though yes, it was silly, I know!)
Andrew arrived, with his new suit on-
Smartly dressed for Jonathans first Communion-
And I was dressed in my tartan trouse,
With my blow-up cushion to sit on (instead of those hard pews!)
And all in all we looked smart and fine,
Ready to receive the Holy bread and wine.
We joined in grace, and sang the songs,
Granted peace, and forgave all wrongs.
Thus, the night that passed was liked by all,
Ending with "All Creatures Great and Small".

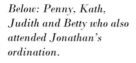

Below: Penny, Kath, Judith and Betty who also attended Jonathan's ordination.

Above and Right: John and Andrew in Lanzarote following Penny's death.

Probably the final photograph of Penny and Andrew cycling together in Derbyshire.

Penny and Andrew at their last Christmas together and Andrew on holiday in Lanzarote. Andrew with Michele on a night out with Penny and the rest of the crowd.

A Message From Mark Burgess, Fellow CF Sufferer and Penny's Friend

At 4 months old I was taken ill with Pneumonia and ended up in hospital for some time. This ultimately lead to a diagnosis of CF after various tests. This was obviously a shock to my parents and family, who knew very little about the disease back in 1971.

During the years that followed, Mum and Dad had to learn pretty quickly how to deal with the illness and the 'do's and don'ts'. As a child I managed to keep fairly well with no hospital admissions until the age of 17. I then didn't have a further one until 27.

As I have got older the illness has progressed but certainly not at the level that would be expected. In fact my parents were told that I wouldn't reach the age of 21.

In 2002 I achieved a BA (Hons) in Graphic Design and have since worked full time as a Graphic Designer/ Studio Manager. I got married to my amazing wife in 2006 and have two wonderful children.

And what does the future hold...?
In Feb 2019 I trialled the new drug Orkambi and have had an improvement in lung function and at the ripe old age of 48 I am looking forward to further new treatments that are in the pipeline!

Above: Penny, Dave Burgess and Mark Burgess preparing for a Fun Run. Dave was Treasurer of the Bolton branch of the Cystic Fibrosis Trust, and Mark, his son, also has Cystic Fibrosis.
Below: Mark with his mum at graduation.

Above: Penny, Michele, Judith and Andrew Morley on a fundraising mission.

Above Top: Mary Yates, who for years used to help with Cystic Fibrosis Bolton. She would assist at jumble sales and in counting the donations after house to house collections, and was involved in many other ways.

Above: More recently, Mark Burgess with his dad and wife Hayley. Read more about Mark's progress on the previous page.

APPENDIX 2:
Some of Penny's Letters, Poems and Pictures

Hello everybody. Here is a lovely puzzle book for Christmas. There are maze's, and lots of other things, and a Crossword. Bye-Bye for now Santa Claus.

As well as being an enthusiastic letter writer, Penny was a talented artist and poet, and it has been a joy to duplicate some examples of her work in this book.

Penny drew and wrote from being very small, and all the cards she sent would be hand made.

When she was in Papworth, it was my birthday. I arrived, and noticed there was a present wrapped up.

Penny, assisted by the nurses, had made a bra from string and bandages and labelled the sides as Left and Right so we'd know which was which.

It was a typical Penny thing to do!

We're birds of a feather so lets stay together.

The Scottish Shore.

If death awaits think only this —
Now I lie in Heavens bliss.
You placed a heart in this withered hand,
That forever loves dear Scottish land.

And if, because I die, you mourn,
Sit in our wood at the break of dawn.
And think of our love, I do implore,
Shared upon the Scottish Shore.

Dumb, beguiling, full of fright,
Quiet, I stole, through the night.
And sleepless shadows clung to me,
As I strode on, quite stubbornly.

If I should die, think only this;

That now I lie in eternal bliss.

You've placed a heart in my withered hand,

That forever loves old Scottish land.

And if, because I die, you're sad

Consider this; things aren't so bad —

Think of the love ~ I do implore ~

Shared, upon that Scottish shore.

Heaven Sent, Taylor Made

Penny, a keen letter writer, wrote to her dad during his stay in Monsall Hospital in 1989, and just a few of her many poems/letters to him are reproduced on the following pages. The letter on the next page was written while Penny was preparing to attend her granddad's funeral.

Hi Dad!

MARCH 30TH 1989.
'Dads stay in Monsall'.

How's the sniffle?
Here's the surprise I told you about :-

You've met the Doctors and the staff,
With some you've even shared a laugh.
You've been to Monsall in all seasons —
Despite the many varied reasons.
And though the car seems drawn by static,
It drives to Monsall automatic.

You've sat in Monsall with your daughter
And cheered her up — as you oughta!
And even flicked the stubborn bubbles
That in her drip caused lots of troubles.

You've swooned at needles, tests and drugs —
Yet had a jab to conquer bugs!
But in the ward, if Doctor passes
Watch Out! He may just do your gasses!!!

Although the food is Cordon "Blurr"...!
And in your throat leaves gravy fur,
Be thankful for the dishwash brew,
That swills away the globby stew.

I know you'll really like it there.
(You're always sending me!)
They'll find a drug, so don't despair —
Just watch that dishwash tea!!

(Hope you like it.)

If you want to know how to escape from that wonderful
holiday camp — the secret is to either drive them mad, or
GET WELL SOON.

Ok!

(And tell them you're allergic to
needles as they bring you out in a rash.)

Woof
woof

FREEWAY
missing you
terribly.

Lots of love. Penny. xxx

Monday.
3rd April 1989. 11·pm.

Tum Te tum.

Hi Dad!

I bet when you receive this you'll be sat there thinking: "It's hard work here, with all the hustle and bustle, jabs, tabs and general activity on the ward — I wonder what's happening at home? I wonder what I'm missing?"

HOME SICK

Well. That's how I was feeling at Marys — "I wonder what's going on at home?" and I felt a wee bit homesick for Freeway. Or is it dogsick?

So at dinner time I nipped home. I'd been up since 6·00am and ironically in this mornings post was a book from CF entitled "Coping with Bereavement". I had a lot of fuss with the keys and couldn't get in the house though the keys fitted the lock. Ten minutes later, with cold hands and a blue nose, I then realised — Yes! these were the front door keys!!!

BEFORE ✓

FTER

Now, I shall tell you now that I think in many ways Ward 7 along with its daily bedlam is nowhere near as busy as Nº 68 here! The phone is no longer in use! Why? Well, it rang so much the plastic got hot and melted. We now have a very arty piece of guey plastic moulded onto the side of the cupboard. It looks quite fetching next to the plastic bin. The doorbell — previously hibernating — has set up a big protest and the last we heard all the bells in our row are on strike. (Inside the house, there was a young girl darting from rapidly melting plastic to an angry doorknob — ME!!) ·Mum was last seen walking round in circles in the kitchen not knowing where she was going next. As you can see, it's lovely and peaceful here. SNORE!

Goodnight.

Quite a few sympathy cards have arrived and the funeral is more or less sorted out. Michele is coming and we are both travelling in Jeans car but I dont know whether we will be standing in Ridgemont with everybody — depends on the weather. Andrew Guilfillans mum & Dad have raised £14 for Cf by asking people along their row. His Dad, and Samanthas mum & Dad, are coming to the funeral too. All the cars have been arranged, and Flatleys are doing the buffet. I think we have it organized.

How are the Doctors treating you? By now you may be suspecting that you are involved with mafia-type folks with all those jabs, but apparently this is all part of the hospital routine. So dont worry.

Have you heard the story about Aunty Dorothys notorious hat? Well, on Sunday Connie, Ruth, Gran & Dorothy went to church with mum. Gran had to sit next to mum so that Mum could find the pages for her, Aunty Ruth was trying to organise everyone, and Aunty Dorothy was being very conspicuous in a large-rimmed black hat. (The only one _in_ a hat too!) When asked where she got the wonderful creation she said it was from a jumble sale and "what a bargain it was". Since then it has been sat under the bed and she had to dust it in order to wear it.

"All things bright and beautiful" was changed to " All things black and curious...."!!

WARNING: THIS LETTER COULD SERIOUSLY DAMAGE YOUR/MY HEALTH (if shown to Aunty Dorothy!)

<u>11·30 pm</u> <u>5· April 89.</u>

Well. Ok - so that was a big interval . I know. But Michele has been here all day. In fact she saw Grandad earlier at Grans and she said he had a lovely blue satiny material on and he looked very very peaceful and happy. She travelled with me in the funeral car and we were also with Jean. Margaret, Andrew Guilfillans dad, and Samanthas Dad Mr Livesy. We walked behind the coffin into church but it was bitter cold. I was upset throughout the service - Michele sat with me and held the prayer sheet for me. Some use that was though because I couldn't read it and said some words wrongly. It's not easy reading through watery eyes !!

During the prayers I almost giggled though because Grans hand decided to dither. And dither it did !! What a racket it seemed to make — the paper in her hand rubbed against her coat you see.

Caused by some confusion Michele and I ended up following the coffin. I think Grandad would have been pleased though as Michele knew him better than any of my mates. However, as our heads were bowed we both nearly walked into the coffin at the church door — typical eh! I can just imagine what it would have been like had we knocked the coffin on the floor.

In fact I was only saying to mum yesterday that it's a good job we managed to seat Rev. Gatenby in one of the funeral cars. we had visions of him having to lie next to the coffin because there was no room in the other 2 cars. I can just see the local rag — "the Rector Denis Gatenby, at the funeral of Mr John Taylor, was very laid back .... !!"

Just what we DON'T need!

Michele and Penny.

The holes in this paper were caused by freeway nails. He stood on it to remind you of him.

Hint
hint!!

<u>Fourth April 1989.</u>

<u>'Allo 'Allo!</u> 'Tis moi here.

'Ow are you?

Mum ses ya want a-nuver letter so 'ah fort "reet! That's waddi wants. That's waddi gets!" <u>YOU ASKED FOR IT</u>!!

However, this time in order to save our skins I'll not mention our beloved relatives — you know who!

(Today I mean)

I rang Andrew up yesterday and he has agreed to drive us to Papworth. As soon as I mentioned it he jumped at the chance thinking, (no doubt), — "great. Another holiday! Yeh!"

Then I said "Of course Andrew, if it will interrupt your work......" to which he hastily cleared his throat and said "Oh...er...yes. Mmm. I'd better investigate the possibilities first... make sure it doesn't upset studying etc......But I'm sure it'll be Ok".

Ha! Any excuse for a holiday.

Anyway. He has said he'll stay till Thursday, visit me whilst he's there, and catch the train back. Good eh!

ANDREW STUDYING...

Today, the house...this house...has been very busy. Hmm. I thought that would surprise you. Our house? Busy? Never! I could give you a list of people who've rung...(yes, we've got a new phone)...but I haven't got so much paper. Or ink.

I get my words muddled now...I say "Yes. It's a shame." when somebody tells me their dog enjoyed its walk etc. because I am so used to saying the same things to folk I now get muddled. Even mum rang Mona only to find that Gran picked up the phone instead. Such is the state of things here!

Goodnight again.

PS// Keith has just come to take Freeway out. (Watch it - you'll be getting a rival!!) Wendy took him earlier whilst it was sunny - she got down Bulls Brew and it REALLY snowed. I mean — mega-blizzard! She was not amused.

"woof woof." X

PEACE

Freeway says "Goodnight." too
(-And good luck tomorrow.)

Imagine if you have to bring a net home too. We could call it "Pen's Den". Can you imagine it.

Wednesday. 5th April 1989.

9.30. I got up at 9.00 am — the phone woke me. I thought "Here we go!" So I staggered down in a semi-trance. A bit like a zombie programmed to make a bee-line for the kettle. And whilst I sat, trying to tune into Wednesday, the phone decided to give me a rude awakening!! And after I'd controlled myself by not throwing it out of the window, Aunty Kath cheerfully said "Hi. How's things this morning". Huh!

10.30 — Anne from Monsall has just rung as you know. Mum is in the bath, Freeway is sat next to me wanting more cuddles — he's frightened because a lot is happening and he's not getting his usual fuss off folk. Don't worry though, he's far from being neglected. And me? Oh, you know, I answer the p..p..ph..phone (Aagh!)

I spoke to Ian. He sends his sympathy and also hopes you're home & well soon. Don't know whether his sympathy was meant for the fact that you are in hospital, or because of Grandad. (I'm sure it's the latter.) I'm going to write this letter at regular intervals so that you know what's happened and don't feel too left out.

Snow White with all this snow ?!?x??! Work that one out eh! Margaret Crank who we met at Papworth rang this morning and is sorry to hear the news. She sends her regards.

I'm going to bed now. I'm shattered. Michele has been a brick today — talk about having a good friend. She's brill. She's made brews and in between talking on the phone we had a good chat about Gran & Grandad. I think it did us both good because she used to go round to their house a lot too. So we've had a good day despite what has happened. The service was lovely, lots of folk, and you got a mention. If you'd been here though you wouldn't have been able to go to the cemetry or Grans either so other than the service you haven't missed a great deal.

Anyway, don't go coming home TOO soon. (I don't want your germs mate!)

LET THEM GET YOU RIGHT FIRST. What's another few days if it gets you better.

Lots of love. x x
x x Penny x & Freeway.
x x x x
x x x x

Heaven Sent, Taylor Made

Above: Penny wrote to Andrew Jackson and his family following the domino transplant. She saw their article in 'Take a Break' magazine, and the two families soon became friends.

68 Church St.
Horwich.
BOLTON.
22nd MAY 1990.

Dear Andrew & family,

Everyone here is so pleased that we've been able to get in touch and it's been the topic of conversation ever since Saturday. My friends think it's great but thought it was inevitable as they said they could tell I was curious from the moment I came across your article.

I've managed to get photocopies of the articles about my transplant for you. Yesterday we had to go to Papworth as I awoke with a bad chest pain so they told us to get there as soon as we could. In the meantime I had a painkiller which meant that by the time we arrived it had gone. They said it could be slight rejection so I've to keep my eye on things. Whilst I was at outpatients I spotted their photocopier so I asked Liz if she'd mind if I photocopied the enclosed. She didn't mind and she also wanted photocopies of both your articles & mine — so we're both going up on the wall at Papworth along with all the other newspaper cuttings etc. There's a wall just full of peoples stories and photos in OutPatients. We only had copies of certain photos so I've tried to pick out my 'famous firsts' ie, first time I stood up etc. I also found one of the van that delivered your heart, which I thought you might be interested in. I don't know about you but we've got a lot of photos of all the stages post op. A long time before my transplant I decided that I would like to have a really good photographic account of each stage of recovery so we'd planned well in advance. The only thing was actually remembering to take the camera with us when we got the call. Luckily, we did! The team in ICU were great and they let Mum & Dad take photos ½ hr after I'd come back from theatre.

This weekend I'm hoping to go caravanning in the Lake District. My friend Andrew and his family have a caravan in Grassmere so we're hoping to go from Friday night 'til Monday. It'll be quite cramped as there's three in his family, and Mum, Dad and I too. It will be the first time I've been caravanning in years! I was telling your mum the other day that I was really very fortunate until I was 18 yrs old. I'd have a few problems with Cf over the years but nothing serious. This meant I had been active and enjoyed school. I was lucky enough to take all my O & A levels and it was only a month or so after my A levels had finished that I realized that my health wasn't good at all. (June 1987) In the February of that year I'd realized that I was becomming more breathless but I was too busy with studying to really take much notice of it. I was also pretty scared so I found it easier to ignore — of course it's easy to look back now and see how silly that was, but at the time heart/lung transplants were relatively new and therefore I'd never even considered that there might be an alternative. Of the Cystics that I'd known in the past, once the deterioration started there was no alternative, and that was a very scary prospect. However, on the last day of December that year, Dr Webb suggested a h/l t/plant to me. Mum & Dad had approached him with the idea then, when he said "Yes. It's a possibility", they asked him to put it to me. I waited 6 months for my assessment, and it was only in January 1989, that they asked me if I would be willing to donate my heart. Of course, I didn't hesitate. After all, it would have just been wasted and now, to see how you are benefitting from it, it makes me realize it was the right decision. I'm just so happy that it's still ticking away ok! (I must admit though that I feel sorry for it - after all, it's to go all through school and exams for a second time! It put some overtime in, I think, the first time round, with all the worry of study and deadlines to be met!)

It may interest you to know that in 1980 (January) we travelled to America - Disneyland - then to New Zealand and finally to Singapore over a period of 7 weeks. Other foreign places It's been to are Yugoslavia, (1979); France (1982) with a school exchange; and Teneife (1988) in an attempt to improve my health. So you see its quite a well travelled little heart.

And of course it's off on its travels again in October.

I used to regularly take part in a 5 mile run around Horwich too, and during the summer I would be constantly cycling miles on my bike. So it should be a tough little heart too.

Anyway. I shall get these articles to you in the post. Thanks again for the lovely flowers — do you know, carnations and that tiny white flower are my favourite. Mum has arranged them in our front window, they look really summery.

Take care and hope to meet you all before long.

Love Penny. xx
x

Ps. Mum & Dad send their regards.

The Classical Periods of Greek Jewellery.

In Greece, between about 575 and 475 BC, jewellery was very rare but after the Persian Wars of 490 and 480-79 BC. it became more plentiful. Jewellery of the classical period – 475 – 330 BC – follows closely in style and technique from what little we know of the period. Filigree was used in decorative patterns, and enamel was becoming more popular. Inlay of stone or glass was very rare.

Towards the end of this period though we find engraved stones in the bezels of finger rings.

Gold filigree-decorated earring from Eretria, Euboea, (Greece). They have green enamelled rosettes and each earring has four tiny pendants in the form of cockle shells.

On top of the crescent sits a Siren. (6cm)

Coiled shape of earring.

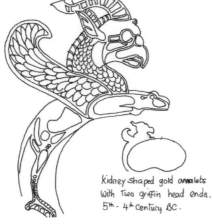

Kidney shaped gold amulets with two griffin head ends. 5th - 4th century BC.

Greek Cypriot Speciality Earrings. 5th century B.C. Spiral, gold plated bronze earrings decorated with blue & green enamel. Griffins heads.

The eye brooch

The eye brooch may be based on the agate eye in Roman amuletic jewellery.

Roman gold ring with a plain sardonyx.

Gold Roman Cameo Ring from the classical period. Set with a cameo depicting the head of Medusa.

Hellenistic Greek Gold Jewellery.

The top is part of a diadem dating to the 3rd century AD. It was found on the island of Melos and is made up of three twisted gold bands, the middle one of which is decorated with rosettes. The reef knot in the centre is richly enamelled and has a large cabochon garnet.

A Greek Signet ring of the 4th century BC. An engraved scene of Aphrodite holding a dove.

Note the comparison between the top diadem with the bottom one which dates from the classical period, 325 BC.

The reef knot here is inlaid with garnets, and the flanking squares of goldwork are decorated with enamel and filigree.*

The Hellenistic age marked the end of the classical period.

* Filigree – A decorative pattern made of wires, sometimes soldered to a background, but often left as open work.

Above: Penny's artwork relating to the classical period - not similar to her other work. You'll see in the photo pages at the end of the book, that Penny's dad, John, produced some wonderful work influenced by the classical periods.

87-88

Night told need Heart. Lung Transplant. (Wrote Article God!) *Coincides with Diary*

"To ride a pale horse to Bambery Cross is not yet my intention"

I, am a picture person; ie, I view things in images. I see my life now as a crossroads with two horrible paths. However, in one picture I see my health declining, constant drips & no hope left. The other more colourful image is the possibility of me on a steep hill taking new, miraculous Deep breaths.
Death is present in either picture; a pale horse watching. But in the second image it is not by my side, but at the foot of the hill. I have been given a chance and I feel it is towards this image that I shall be guided.

May 88 I put all my energy into being 'happy' and the 'sad' will therefore only show its ugly head when my energy has been spent.
I doubt therefore sadness will show too often

July 22. I just cried at night, I feel weak and scared. Thank goodness I have my faith in God.
I think I would have cracked up otherwise.
Every night I talk and talk to God. It helps so much: He always lets me sleep!

Aug 10th Mum and I went in church to pray.
Jan 25th Christy Nolan, under the eye of the clock, inspired Penny to write to him, and to do her own biography.

(Humor) Weather Cool.
July 18th John Duckworth begins employment at Fort Sterling producing toilet rolls.
(Talk about starting at the bottom)

Come fly with me!

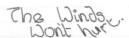

The Winds Won't hurt.

TEDDY PLANTER

Use to be a healthy bear. He enjoyed playing with his friends, though he had to wrap up when the cold winds blew. He didn't like the wind – it made him breathless.

Teddy Planter was very poorly. He found it very difficult to breathe, and he couldn't eat his food.

Then, one day, a Dr came up with a very good idea – a heart/lung Transplant.

After his Transplant, Teddy felt so much better and began to build up his wasted muscles on an exercise bike.

Now Teddy can go out in the wind and breathe easily. He's a happy bear now.

Some of Penny's pottery creations from her time early on at high school.

Heaven Sent, Taylor Made

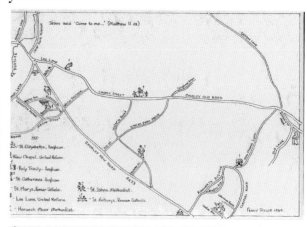

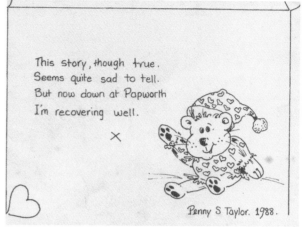

Above: Pictures and postcards from when Penny's voice was in a bad way.
Also, a map Penny produced of her local area, showing all the churches.

FAMILIAR FRIENDS

When awesome death is by my side
And all the mourner's here have cried,
Old friends shall crowd the grave. For in
The lull that follows tears, a host
Of sentiment appears.

              Youths old ghost
Shall preach about my corpse, within
Open wounded earth.

              But those
Who mourned my birth, shall be
Of a stranger familiarity:
Knowledge and wisdom - tall and proud,
Wrapped up in orthodoxy's clothes -
Shall sing, shall dance, shall laugh aloud:
"Oh, the life is now no more!
Life's individuality
Now lies with immortality.
She's crossed to the sleeper shore!"

(Maybe, maybe, Love is there,
With passionate eyes, and lips and hair..)

And soon a sensibility
will enter grieving hearts, to be
The handkerchief of time, of years;
Thus satisfying human tears.
Wisdom shall wisely creep away
To other hearts on which to play.
But knowledge....sweet knowledge.... will ever rest
It's head upon my breast.

There to guard those left behind,
Happiness, and hope, shall lead the 'blind'.

And peace shall guide the dead.
             So crown
The head; with thistle and pink rose.
Welcome hopefulness, and joy!
             Down
On the pathway, leading to home-
Stirring grass and trees- they roam:
Happiness, and hope, in country clothes.

A reason will, in later years
Ride past and steal your darkest fears.
But memories will be your smile;
Laughing, and laughing, all the while...

WHO NEEDS WINGS TO FLY?

Why can't I be a bird?
I, too, need my freedom!
You say to me, "have you not heard?
Freedom's only entitled to some!"

So why not me? I ask.
Do I not deserve to be let loose;
Loose, into the unknown task,
Of which I'd make use?!

"I don't want to be a bird", I say.
Who needs wings to fly?!
No, I'll make the most of each day,
And when tomorrow comes, I'll say "Goodbye".

'BEDTIME' BLUES

Hello   . I've time on my hands!
I'm tucked up in bed with no cares or demands.
The Doctor, he's told me to 'sit down and rest'
If I want to avoid a bad pain in my chest.
The problem, it started on Sunday at eight-
I couldn't get up, as I went to bed late!
But I had to get going, for at ten we were due
At Manchester Cathedral, in time for a pew.
So I dashed round the house and gulped down my food-
Half was uneaten, and half was unchewed-
But by quarter past nine we were all on our way
And much looking forward to the rest of the day.
We arrived in good time- a few minutes we'd gained-
All set to watch Jonathan being ordained.
Whilst walking along, we met him arriving-
He was happy and beaming, though glad not to be driving!
This was to be a big day in his life
And we would all witness, along with his wife,
The service in which this young man would cease
To be deacon; for now we could call him a priest.
So the service began, and we sat at the front!-
Yes, we could see everything, from Altar to Font-
And gleaming and sparkling the Bishop walked in,
Followed by a line of his holy men.
All were dressed up, in gold, white and red,
Clutching their Bibles and bowing their head.
The sight was stupendous and held us in awe-
Then prayers soon followed, according to Gods Holy Law.
And then we were singing, a tune bright and gay,
But suddenly a problem came clouding my day:
I'd sung the first verse, for the second I waited,
When...boom, boom, boom,... my heart palpitated!
It gave me a panic, I sat down real quick,
Though not knowing what to do made me feel quite sick.
With luck it subsided, and beat back to norm,
By then I felt tired, and a little forlorn.
The service, it finished, some time around noon
And by one we were home. I went up to my room.

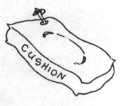

All afternoon though, I felt bright and breezy-
No sign of a cough. And I didn't feel wheezy.
So, at 6.22, I decided to go
To church (though yes, it was silly, I know!)
Andrew arrived, with his new suit on-
Smartly dressed for Jonathans first Communion-
And I was dressed in my tartan trouse,
With my blow-up cushion to sit on (instead of those hard pews!)
And all in all we looked smart and fine,
Ready to receive the Holy bread and wine.
We joined in grace, and sang the songs,
Granted peace, and forgave all wrongs.
Thus, the night that passed was liked by all,
Ending with "All Creatures Great and Small".

But going home I clutched my chest
And a thought crossed my mind- "I need to rest!"
Too late! A pain shot up my back and side-
It hurt so much I nearly cried-
I couldn't talk, or walk, or moan,
So Dad and Andrew carried me home.
Once there, I sat down in a chair
And didn't move, (I didn't dare!)

However, now the pain has gone.
Doctor says its "exhaustion",
I went for X-rays yesterday,
And the results took all my fears away.
For first, a phnuemothorax threatened-
This was hard to comprehend-
But when I saw that all was sound,
My optimism once again was found.

I'm under orders now to rest
(Which really is a tiresome pest!)
But Doctor says it will restore my zest,
So I must believe that he knows best.

And you know how boring it can be
To sit in bed and watch T.V.
So whilst I'm here and getting better,
I couldn't resist writing you this letter!

Lots of love,

Tear shaped (Earths tears)

(Diamond shaped like eyes.)

(pearl shaped) is a pearl droplet.

"THE PINE CONE."

The woods bore your jewelled form;
An egg-shelled paradigm of pearls, oozed
And washed by the enigmatically veiled sap-store;
The syrupy, honeyed liquid of Earths bowels, born,
And flowing, and indeed used
Primarily, to flush out these hesitant tears of Earths core.

The woods raised your jewelled form;
The ever-guiding, ever-guarding mid-wife
That witnessed your primitive, diamond-blinking eyes;
Those radient hues that project warm,
Mysterious overtones of opulent life.

Yet still, and now, the kernel cries.

The woods admired your jewelled form;
You were the 'fruit' that tempted their serpentine curves.
And yeilding scintillations congregated perpetually.

The olivine leaves have since conformed to your forlorn,
Debased beauty. Periwinkled amethysts now aware of your
                                    esoteric preserves.
For although disguised, Earths rich tears still lament
                                    willingly.

By Penny Taylor.
14th July 1987.

SETH.
(CF)

Seth, is a constant companion:
Like the old, worn coat of my youth.
Cosseting!
Comforting!
All embracing!
Guarding me, protecting me, from
                    Winters chill ...
Seth, is a steadfast foe.
He wears himself, with ease, upon me;
Around me.
Flung!
Well fitted!
Fixed! In place.
And now, as
            my
                hands
                    dig
                        deeper
Into his familiar, warm pockets,
He slowly buttons himself,
            Tightly, around my chest...

When's the stag night?

you can keep my phone buzzy anytime!

I think you're toadally wonderful!

I think its twins!

How about a beetle drive

PURRFECT.

OLD NECTAR HEARTS VISION.

I did enjoy June...Its now a far and lovely vision. The glorious white sun caused my young heart to blossom with a rich, sweet love...the nectar of that pulsating organ that lies deep within me. Do you never have that feeling, though, that you have met with other eyes, before you had time to kiss the lovely ones goodbye? Do you never sense that societies cruel lawful ties have gagged you before you've had time to relate your tale? Does life not send you spinning with no suggestion of ease...like a fierce keeper, forcing you to create pebbles from huge boulders of solid rock? Then this, my love, is the price we must pay for our vision...the wonderful vision we created that summer.
Only when the vision returns will we be freed.
And lovely eyes will meet again. (Old Nectar Heart is stubborn)!

```
                                        Two lovers met. He still,
                                        Content to be. She curious with a rare
                                        Resolute heart, beating him
                                                              against his will–
Night was in its glorious hour;         Till love fused the pair.
The hour of birth, when daylight entered.
And flowers lifted their prostrate heads
To witness the fine birth.
```

And June passed by, allowing Winter to dominate the stage. And sun made way for the harsh sting of frost to mercilessly stab the flowers to death; to tear the colourful display of leaves from the branches; and to inject its deadly glacial poison into the small vulnerable creatures until they sprawled lifeless, at last, onto the icy floor of Earth. (Only Old Nectar Heart survived).
And so this continued each year. Each bitter Winter passing, to make way for summers liturgy to return: The wayside flowers were warmed and healed so that they could once more blossom; the trees' were granted fruitfulness again; and the creatures were awakened by the magnificent rays of the white sun.
There was, each year, a huge, tremendous reunion of nature. (But Old Nectar Heart remained alone, awaiting for the vision to reappear.)

```
              "He wears
The ungathered blossom of quiet; stiller he
Than a deep well at noon, or lovers met;
Than sleep, or the heart after wrath. He is
The silence following great words of peace."
                              R. Brooke.
```

PENNY TAYLOR.

PRIVATE.

```
Andrew, something for you to read,

Though a few clues yet we still need.

I'll give you a ring in a day or two,

And then we'll arrange what we can do.

We need to go to Rivi Green,

And see what clues there can be seen.

Then we need to visit the pub,

To organize the supper, I think we should.

Hope you like all this rhyme.

See you in a few days time!
                              Pen.
```

An envelope from when Penny and Andrew Morley organised a treasure hunt!

THE RARE NIGHT.

Tonight I saw the sky
Grow dark with age.
Still was yet stiller by
This lamplit stage.
Moon breathed. Tides swelled,
And sea, with Eden, filled.
This night was rare.
And whilst darkness dreamed,
You slept, and seemed
So peaceful there.
How long could this night last?
No pleasant hours spoke
But these!
So today, just to please,
I awoke.
And three long years had past.

11th April 1988

Life before birth.

My mind knows not of books and art
For here my life prepares to start.
My house is but a jelly fish wall;
An orbiting tunnel for my hall.

I wish to learn; I want to know
What lies beyond my head or toe.
I see no shapes, I know no words;
I know not yet of silk throat birds.

What is good? And what is bad?
Am I a girl, or a lad?
Patience is my virtue here
And I must wait for near' a year.

I'm unaware of day or night,
The sun is distant, far from sight.
I know my time is nearly through,
And plans I'll make before I'm due.

For I was chosen for this 'play'
I'll act my part both night and day.
Yet from my thoughts I never ran;
I was born and my dream began.

Terry S Taylor.

People Crossing

Norman boat.

You know, we've got to stop meeting like this!

Swim up my stream anytime

Red Tunic Soldiers.

Flickering, on distant hills from where I
Stood, breathing their red hue 'cross marbled sky,
Were the lights of my land. Hushed, in the night.
And seen, by my vantage, an owls lone flight.

We three, in silence, wait: Desolate road,
I, and the sequent trees, in bated mode.
No creature joined and I was glad. But yet,
The night! Affable, though we had not met.

At least, not here! Upon this splendid hill
Where the cool air whistled along the still
Road, in a windy tune. This was the hour!
All successive thoughts emanate this store.

I waited, breathless. Dawdled other hours
In those places that I could only scour.
Mine had no thought as I sat, content, here.
(This, my secret hour. And the time was near!)

Soon, I felt the chill, and the stir, of change.
And night, its visitant darkness attained.
At last! The midnight view I came to see —
Lights, like red-tunic soldiers, stood. For me!

26TH February 1989.

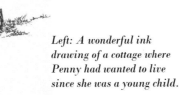

Left: A wonderful ink drawing of a cottage where Penny had wanted to live since she was a young child.

You sound like the one for me!

Ant we a pair!

You may be a 'Dragon', but I'll 'fly' with you anytime!

Batty about you!

Penny. August 1988

Perfection comes naturally to some of us.

'Ant anybody to love me!

Care to try?

Alpen

Dear Penny,

how are you? In your last letter you asked me if I done Graphics at school, well the answer is no. We don't have such a thing at our school. By the way I recieved a letter from The Prince and Princess of Wales on Monday, I was dead chuffed. I might send one to Margaret Thatcher. What do you think? This week I am sending a letter to Princess Alice and Princess Margaret. Guess what we are getting? another budgie I think it will be yellow.

My Mum has been nagging at me all week! she keeps saying 'If you don't stop moaning and start doing a little piece of work now and then you will not be going to Penny's in Easter' So I have to shut up! And to top it all Jayne has gone crazy over another boy. (I just can't take much more). She's ill just now though so she doesn't get to see him very often so instead she talks on and on and on about him which is very depressing as you can imagine.

By the way, the Alpen sign has blown off so I shall renew it on shoppingday when we get some Alpen.

Thankyou for your photograph of the alpens it is very nice. I showed it to my mates and they say you are a fabulous artist.

Lots of love
Alan
xxx
xx
x

P.S Tell Julie it's almost certain I shall come at Easter.

Penny and Alan McBurnie (her mum's cousin's son) were pretty close from an early age, and the combination of their names led to the 'Alpen' joke, as can be seen in some of their early correspondence. Alpen referred to an area of woodland near Alan's home.

Above: Alan and his family with Penny.
Below: Alan and Penny.

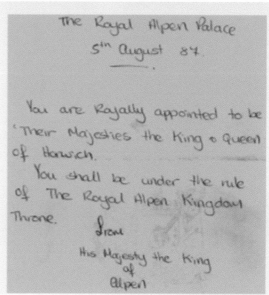

The Royal Alpen Palace
5th August 84.

You are Royally appointed to be 'Their Majesties the King & Queen of Harwich.

You shall be under the rule of The Royal Alpen Kingdom Throne.

from
His Majesty the King of Alpen

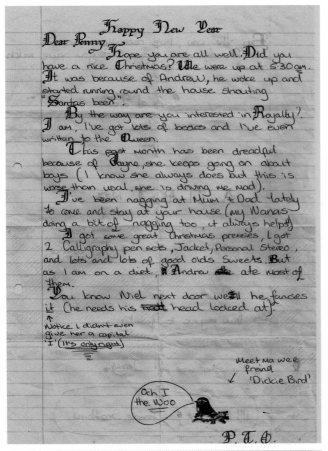

Happy New Year

Dear Penny,
Hope you are all well. Did you have a nice Christmas? We were up at 5·30am. It was because of Andrew, he woke up and started running round the house shouting "Santas been".

By the way are you interested in Royalty? I am, I've got lots of books and I've even written to the Queen.

This past month has been dreadful because of Jayne, she keeps going on about boys (I know she always does but this is worse than usal, she is driving me mad).

I've been nagging at Mum + Dad lately to come and stay at your house (my Nanas doing a bit of nagging too, it always helps)

I got some great Christmas pressies, I got 2 Calligraphy pen sets, Jacket, Personal Stereo, and lots and lots of good olds Sweets. But as I am on a diet, Andrew ate most of them.

You know Niel next door we'll he fancies it (he needs his head looked at)

↑ Notice I didnt even give her a capital
I (It's only right)

Meet Ma wee freind
↙ 'Dickie Bird'

Och I the Woo

P.T.O.

THE ROYAL SEAL OF APPROVAL.

FROM HIS MAJESTY THE KING OF THE ROYAL ALPEN KINGDOM

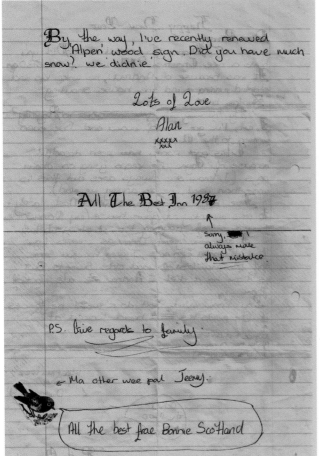

By the way, I've recently renewed 'Alpen' wood sign. Did you have much snow? we didnie.

Lots of Love
Alan
xxxx
xxx

All The Best In 1987

↑ Sorry, I always make that mistake.

P.S. Give regards to family.

← Ma other wee pal Jenny.

All the best frae Bonnie Scotland

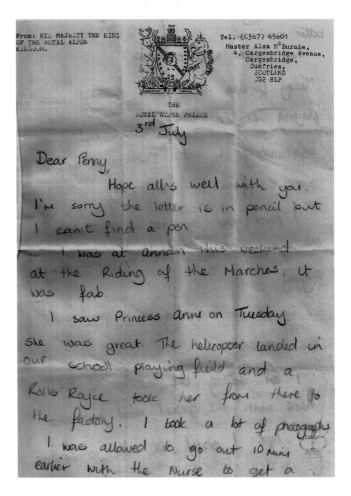

From: HIS MAJESTY THE KING OF THE ROYAL ALPEN KINGDOM.

Tel. (0387) 65801

Master Alan McBurnie,
4, Cargenbridge Avenue,
Cargenbridge,
Dumfries,
SCOTLAND
DG2 8LP

THE ROYAL ALPEN PALACE

3rd July

Dear Penny,
Hope all's well with you. I'm sorry the letter is in pencil but I can't find a pen.

I was at Annan this weekend at the Riding of the Marches. It was fab.

I saw Princess Anne on Tuesday she was great. The helicopter landed in our school playing field and a Rolls Royce took her from there to the factory. I took a lot of photographs I was allowed to go out 10 mins earlier with the Nurse to get a

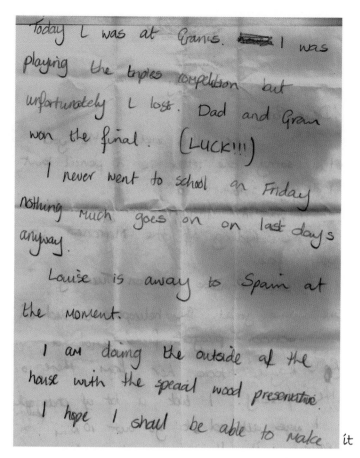

Today I was at Gran's. I was playing the triples competition but unfortunately I lost. Dad and Gran won the final. (LUCK!!!)

I never went to school on Friday nothing much goes on on last days anyway.

Louise is away to Spain at the moment.

I am doing the outside of the house with the special wood preservative. I hope I shall be able to make it

Above: Penny and Alan McBurnie.

Below: Penny's painting of a couple under a tree in the Alpen wood.

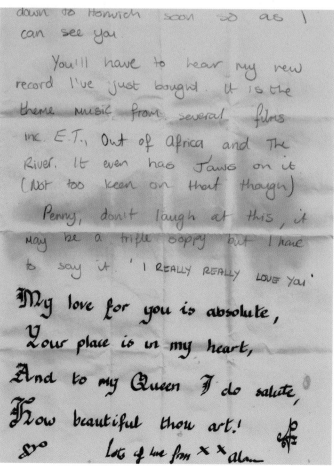

down to Horwich soon so as I can see you.

You'll have to hear my new record I've just bought. It is the theme music from several films inc. E.T., Out of Africa and The River. It even has Jaws on it (Not too keen on that though)

Penny, don't laugh at this, it may be a trifle soppy but I have to say it. ' I REALLY REALLY LOVE YOU'

My love for you is absolute,
Your place is in my heart,
And to my Queen I do salute,
How beautiful thou art!
xo   Lots of love from X X Alan

My Fella.

Sitting in the local temp
I sat, and sketched the folk.
A cartoon slowly filled my page,
Whilst I waited for my bloke.

"He's working late" said the chap,
(This I overheard).
I tried to find out more of him,
But no one really cared.

I supped my tea and eyed the clock,
A fella squeezed my knee.
I turned to him and said some words,
Then packed and went for tea.

He didn't ring that night at home,
What was I to think?
But I saw him on the bus today
And smiled at his secret wink.

HOLIDAY IN BELMONT
1988
(AT JEAN & ANDREW KEELYS)

Thanks for letting us use your home,
It was rather different from being at our own.
The traffic's much quieter. The view, quite serene.
Not like at Church St, where motorists are mean!

No plans for the day, just do as we please;
"If you go out, don't forget keys!"
A trip in the car, or meal up the road;
And then to return to our holiday abode.

Home once more and so to bed,
Maybe a 'Beano' could then be read!!
I hope that Paul is not annoyed,
His comic book was much enjoyed.

One or two friends popped over for tea,
And then we played poole - best out of three!
All in all our week was complete,
Thank you again for this holiday treat.

We stayed at Jean & Andrews
whilst they had a week in the
Lake District, 3rd September — 10th
September 1988

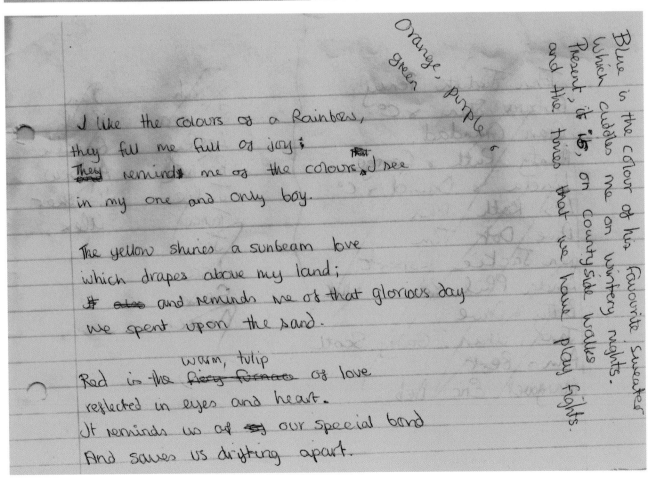

I like the colours of a Rainbow,
they fill me full of joy;
They reminds me of the colours I see
in my one and only boy.

The yellow shines a sunbeam love
which drapes above my land;
and reminds me of that glorious day
we spent upon the sand.

warm, tulip
Red is the of love
reflected in eyes and heart.
It reminds us of our special bond
And saves us drifting apart.

Orange, purple, green.

Blue is the colour of his favourite sweater
Which cuddles me on wintery nights.
Present it on countryside walks
and the times that we have play fights.

In the last few weeks before Penny died, Penny was in the bedroom with her mum and Auntie Margaret. Penny told her mum that if she and dad saw a rainbow, it would be her. For Auntie Margaret it would be a palette of colours.

Heaven Sent, Taylor Made

Hello Aunty Margaret. It's Penny here –
At <u>last</u> your work of Art appeared!
And though it's delivered a cheery smile
It's certainly travelled many a mile.
On the 13th of April at ten-fortyfive,
It hopped in the mail van and went for a drive.
It drove out of Eccles and hit the A1 –
And that's the moment it's travels begun.
Straight into Papworth, it arrived without fuss –
(Though it previously considered catching a bus!)
But then it was sent to C.M.U.
And the nurses cried out – "What can we do?"
"You're far too late", the Doctor said,
"We sent her home. You've been misled".
And soon the letter began to fear –
It's greatest worry being clear –
That 'Penny Taylor' left on Sunday
(And today was surely well past Monday!)
And so the letter was very sad
For things were looking bleak and bad.
It's one way ticket had got it here,
But homeward fares are just as dear,
And 19p's a lot of dosh –
Well, it means 'First Class'. So it must be posh!

The letter knew it's only hope would be
That C.M.U. might pay the fee!
But soon the pen crossed out it's name
And took it back, from where it came.
So at the office near the entrance gate,
There, the letter, was forced to wait.

And then the letter received a fright –
As people were going home for the night.

Not knowing then, how long he'd be,
Letter longed for company:
The stamp, she was a stuffy square,
And brightly sat in a corner chair.
(But then the Royals are upper-class folk –
So maybe <u>that's</u> why she never spoke!)
But there was Frank, sat next to Queen,
Who laughed –"It's not as bad as it might seem!
They'll get us home, just wait and see –
And if they don't, they'll deal with me!"
Soon they started idle chat –
Frank and Letter – about this and that.
And when the sun began to rise
Frank and Letter rubbed their eyes
In disbelief, for they were on their way –
In another van, heading up the motorway.
And though they toured Le Mans Crescent
At least in Bolton they were present.
And then not knowing where else to go
They decided to drop in on Daubhill P.O.
(Of Little Lever they'd had their fill –
Surely their answer could be found at Daubhill?!!)
But from there they were sent to a 'Unit of Chest'
Where a lady and computer looked up Pens address.
She'd opened up Letter and read his insides –
And the contents had duly brought tears to her eyes.
So she'd set about finding where Letter was heading:
(Certainly not Cambridge, or South towards Reading!)
And when she was sure that she'd found the right place
She came in the car to meet Pen face to face.
And Pen was so pleased when she saw Frank and Letter;
(Immediately she felt just so much better!)
And though some might say his arrival is fate,
Most people agree, that Letter is great!

BLISSFUL WANDERINGS.

Death, awaits us all. And I shall leave my friends.
But first, upon this fine land that lends
Its glory to secret valleys, springs, and hills
Where lie the timid beasts; the flowers; and moan
The captured winds; I shall roam.
My mind will rest awhile amongst the daffodils.
And the soft, scented murmurings of nymphs shall forever
Dwell in my breast.

           And there will never
Be a sight more lovely, or complete, than
The firm swellings of Earth; these ancient grassy mounds
Upon which our ancestors began.
And all those aged sports! The fox. And hounds
With teeth, and snarl, and steadfast run.
Followed, by the urgent sounds of man and horse!
Where now – upon this beaten course –
Nettles, and leaves, sprawl endlessly.

        And high, the golden sun.

Penny and her beloved Auntie Margaret. Margaret and her daughter, Deborah, spent lots of time with Penny. Margaret would regularly write, and Penny would reply in the form of poems. Soon, Margaret began to reply in the same way.

27TH FEBRUARY 1989.

Heaven Sent, Taylor Made

Cor, Aunty Margaret, I'm still on Cloud 9.
There's so much to tell you, and so much more time.
It all happened so fast on the 16th November :
So much to say ! So much to remember !
We put down the phone and panic began,
But soon we calmed down and started to plan.
We rang up our driver and said, "Come ! S.O.S !"
He was there by the time I'd packed and was dressed.
We hurled all the luggage, and stuff in the car,
Then started our journey, unknown and afar.
I rang a few friends on the handy car phone,
And told them for Christmas I planned to be home.
Our time passed so quickly — just two and a half hours —
But the time that then followed was no longer ours.
We dashed upto surgical — happy yet scared —
To see if the donor was there. Had they heard ?
The hour that soon followed was loaded with tests —
Bloods, forms, and questions ! No time for rests !
By 2.00 I had signed and was thus on my way —
Laughing and joking. No sign of dismay !
I think that dear sister had slipped in a pill
That made sure my mind with nice thoughts did fill !!
Then Burnie, the nurse, took hold of my hand
Whilst lines were then fitted. (The bit I can't stand !)
But be reassured, I felt little pain —
Then the next thing I knew I come round again !
And faces, so anxious, were watching me there.
My mind was so dreamy, yet I could still hear:
Voices, so soft, and gentle, and kind —
Mum, and Dad, and all my friends behind !!
I was happy - so happy - I felt fit to burst,
But the looks on their faces seemed to fear for the worst.
I couldn't decide why they looked so concerned !
I felt quite cocooned. And safe. And returned.
And I wanted to reach them and tell them how good
My insides were now feeling — Like I knew they just would
I smiled, and I waved, and I held up my thumbs,
(But my mind couldn't count, or calculate sums !!)
'Goodfa' was brought from Sharon and Paul —
He's a cuddly soft dog, though not very tall ;
But he's especially good at giving those hugs
That are needed much more for fighting the bugs !
I had no pain at all up in I.C.U.
I was flat on my back so there wasn't much to do !

But I felt so contented, unaware of the lines,
So I couldn't help dreaming of near happier times.
The worst part of all — and I say this sincere —
(Just the mere thought of it filled me with fear !) —
Was the moment they switched the ventilator off
And I was expected to breathe ! (Very eerie stuff !!)
But I soon got the hang, and I gasped lovely air —
I could breathe in so deeply without any care.''
And later I lay, my lungs starbed to dry —
I felt each cavity opening — it was so good I could cry.
First, the top cavities, burst like a flower,
Followed by others, bigger and lower.
And as they breathed life, and opened up wide,
Like two tiny butterfly wings opening inside,
My nails rushed to pink and my lips followed soon —
I was warm to my toes. Just over the moon !
The changes were beautiful — so gradual and true —

And as I came round I blinked, and I knew
That I was so healthy, like never before :
Never had I breathed till the air hit my core !
It knocked me so dizzy, I spun to a high
And all week I remained with my head in the sky.
The tubes were soon out, just a few still remain —
And now I can chatter 'till I'm nearly insane.
Why, even on Thursday I got on the bike
And wheeled for 10 minutes and talked as I liked.
I left them all speechless — the Doctors and staff —
My legs are so strong ! I just have to laugh !
Aunty Margaret, I wish you could see how I look —
Chubby cheeks, red and rosy — without wine being took !!
My skin's turning soft, and subtle, and pink —
No more rouge needed ! Doesn't it make you think.'
And as for my meals — well, how can I explain —
They slide down so quickly, my weight's soon to gain.
The food they prepare, it tastes so divine —
Even the tea is like heavenly wine !
But best part of all was the first time in years
Healthy me LOOKED at me — Gosh, it brought on the tears.
I stored at the mirror and thought that it lied —
But that healthy pink glow, it could not hide.
My only main problem is voicing my views —
My voice is a whisper as it tells folk the news !
The vocal chords tingled when my tube was in place —
So a tiny wee voice now escapes from my face.

But all is not lost, it's stronger each day —
I'll soon be nattering loudly away.
I feel for the nurses each time they come in —
I tell them each progress, each time and again.
But now I must go for my carriage awaits —
Well, a bike actually — my heart palpitates !
It can hardly wait now to step on the bike,
(Just wait till I tell it we're conquering the Pike !!!)
Oh, I could go on, and on, in this way —
But maybe I'll save it till a healthier day.
Yes, it's true, the bad news is that I am NOT better —
Mr Wallwork informed me that I WILL be fitter !
What can I expect ? Can this all be true ?
All my birthdays are here — I'm no longer blue !
I cannot imagine how well I shall be —
Only the future will let me be free.
But now I remain, stunned and in shock !
Yes, I'm happy, - so happy - so please do not mock.
I'm floating back down from my cloud in the sky.
Give me some time whilst I laugh and I sigh.
It's GREAT. Just so GREAT, to take in some air —
I breathe till I'm dizzy. I just couldn't care.
So I'll finish my poem and send love and kisses —
From us 'both' now I guess — my donor and his missus ! —
It's my first live - in boyfriend, he helps me to move,
And for once my mum and my dad can approve !
So 'Goodbye' for now — my heart palpitates ;
With pleasure, of course, My bike ride awaits !!

*Above: Written by Penny after her transplant, and once she'd
come off the ventilator. She is clearly
delighted that her body is working as it should!*

If we were there...

No more, the chilly breath unites
Our love upon a moonlit kiss.
... High, within our cool clouded wood.
In low grasses no touch excites
Now, the first rosiness of bliss.

... Yet, with opportune, our hearts would!

Penny Taylor.
3rd October 1989.

MY TWO LOVERS.

(DAY.)

Oh, Day. Look! Your head bows. And your body,
Leaning on the lurid stars, in sleep!
Go now, from your lover. Already
Your white light is a faint peep.

Great lover of your hours, am I.
(Lover, of your gentle wake).
But sleep arrests, and now I cry —
"Run! Run from your lover! Forsake!"

I'll wait. And doubtless, you shall come —
Wide-eyed with sun, and childish play!
(Ha! Night, and its Heaven!— Laugh, as they run!)
And you, in my arms. Oh Day!

(NIGHT.)

Day, inhaled into the nostrils of swarthy moon,
left me alone. Dreams, eddying above my head.
Whiteness passed away and a mute lover - Sir Night - soon
billowed softly through the door, and stole upon my bed.

28TH FEBRUARY 1989.
Bie,

The Dam.

Thin anorak flung around your shoulders
(And I with thin blue), hoisting bathed boulders
From the resilient brook, we stood. And cursed
The culprits who'd blocked the hot-tempered burn.
But joy! As you slipped, and the current burst
In anger, and thrust you aside. ~~Then~~ In turn,
You, tremulous and soaked, fell against me ....
"Strange" we laughed "how wet the water can be!!"

In June of this year, I wrote continuously asking you to publisize the need for more donors on your programme. It pleased me immensely when you agreed to invite my friends brother onto the programme, in order to attempt to open the public eyes and make them more aware of this serious problem - the shortage of donors.

Sarah Justin, a cystic fibrosis victim, was seriously ill in Monsall Hospital, Manchester, at that time and has only hope of surviving was a heart and lung transplant. Having known her for two years I felt desperate to help her, but the only way that I was able was to write to you. The devestation I felt when she died only three days following Pauls appearance on your show, is impossible to explain.

It saddened me that that particular show was the last in the series — and that the new series only starts in January.

I have recently written a poem which describes the hurt and frustration that is felt when a dear friend, awaiting the same operation as yourself, dies so suddenly. I have now been on Papworth Hospitals heart and lung transplant waiting list for 16 months, for the same reason as Sarah. I desperately want people to realise what it is like to build up hopes of a new life, and also of the terrible tragedy when friends die with whom you have shared so many good times and bad times.

I would be unable to travel to the studio but I would be so pleased if you would read this poem, in its entirety, on your first programme in the new series. Maybe, if it is read with the understanding that it demands, it would help people to think afresh about signing a donor card and more importantly, discussing their wishes with their families.

Above: A letter from Penny trying to get publicity for transplantation issues. Penny refers to a BBC programme on which her friend's brother appeared. This was Paul, Sarah Justin's brother. Oddly, on this programme, also appeared a little boy called Andrew Jackson who became the eventual recipient of Penny's heart.

The Ungathered Flower.

As brown washed its softness over the lake,
Lone shadows crept from the waters break.
And there, all silent in its grandeur stood
The castle. With frail, broken clouds for its hood.

And dark. So dark, the trees' stooped;
Over the shores, where the grasses drooped
Their solemn heads in quiet repose,
And kissed the bluebell's chilly nose.

Then soft, sneezed the bluey dome;
Across the pebbled shores to roam.
Beneath the stone, rose azure mists,
Tinted with purple, and rare amethyst.

So, as the ungathered flower, lingering afar,
Shows its ghostly hue 'pon the reservoir,
A peace erupts and skims this phantom breeze;
Over the water, to the blue-mist ruins. And trees.

2nd February 1989.
Penny Taylor.
(45 mins)

Heaven Sent, Taylor Made

OH WITCH 'DE L'ARBRES'.

Oh Witch, Oh Which, Horwich, with its trees',
How your landscape has changed to austere.
Once cushioned with roe and swelled with oak leaves,
Now no glimpse of this woodland, I fear.

What happened to your acres of densly clumped bark,
Did you burn it as fuel for your fire?
No nesting place left for your Magpie or Lark;
Except on those lands which are higher.

Choked by smoke from your engines, your trees' became sparse?
Or was it your cotten cloth mills?
Whate'er it was, it seems such a farce,
To have lost your esteem for your ills.

So why not bring back your numerous groves,
Have done with your industrial power.
Raise your hand then, I beg, and cast off your robes;
Wave your wand, Oh Witch 'De L'arbres'.

4TH MAY 1987.

A SPOKE IN THE CYCLE OF LOVE.

They roved to their realm on a cycle of love,
Down a patchwork of small country lanes.
They passed between waters that fell from above,
And spoke about peering through pains.

The misty hued windows reflected their fear,
Yet they cautiously crept inside.
Once in, they found steps in this unspoken lair,
With a trapdoor deceptively guised.

They climbed up the rungs, a reciprocal mount,
Till at last they attained such a height.
And once at the top of this splendid viewpoint,
They looked down at their previous plight.

The roof, it was ashen with rafters and beams,
They explored this amazement of grove.
But once on the ground, on well-wooded greens,
They continued their pedalling rove.

And now they've returned to those renovate flats,
A sad sorry sight for sore feet,
The water's still there, enhanced by the gnats',
Along Rivingtons famous old 'street'.

4TH MAY 1987.

Daisy Chain.

Lonely, in the rugged glade,
  Where love lies sleeping there,
            I made
  A dainty ring of daisy chain,
  Entwined with thoughts of love,
            and pain.

Then swift, I placed this precious charm
  Around your wrist of tattooed arm.
Your eyes, your smile, did happy seem,
  As there sat I, with conjoured dream.

But when I woke to silent air,
  I blinked, and thought I
    saw you there —
  With daises round
    your fair, fair head
  Yet there was I —
    tucked up in bed.

25 January 1989.

Penny S. Taylor.

Tangiwai

He fought the war of youthful cries,
With burnished bum and cornered sighs.
He learnt the rules of wrong and right...
This helped Tangiwai through his plight.

He saw descent and witnessed birth,
He sprung at death yet wept with mirth.
Tangiwai grew both strong and wise,
Within my mortal, laughing eyes.

He knew of patience put to test;
With loves enigma, he knew best.
But Tangiwai was no Crocodile...
More the Serpent, of the Nile.

For Tangiwai came, quite unawares.
Tangiwai proved, to you, he cares.
Take him with you, though he's mine,
For this would aid our breech of time.

REGARDLESS.

A hare eyed tramp in a moth eaten coat,
A sailor with his travelling boat;
A tall, ambiguous pessimist,
A patient with a sebaceous cyst.

A scotsman clad in sporran'd kilt,
A bricky with the wall he built;
An Earl, a Duchess, Queen an' all,
A cricketer with bat and ball.

And don't forget the new born lamb,
The Pig...a juicy slice of ham.
The Cheshire cat with cunning smile,
And the athlete that ran a mile.

But does it know...the Mad March hare...
Or even more, does it care,
That in this world of turmoiled mess,
Life drags on...Regardless?

KINGFISHER BLUE.

Who are you, Kingfisher Blue,
Colour crayoned flash of light?
Orange streak;
Sharp beak;
Where, go you, at night?

You're unlike all my feathered friends,
No time to hear my words.
Magpie listens;
Crows eye glistens;
Oh, such friendly birds!

But you are you, dear Kingfisher Blue,
You'll never change your ways.
Shy you may be;
Hiding from me;
But mabie I'll see you...
                    One of these days!

PALE EYES.

Pale eyes met on green.

Liked, laughed and loved.

Secrets passed unseen,

(Except by the cool sky above).

And pale eyes met hurt.

Years witnessed tears,

And secrets passed. But

Love condemned all fears.

For pale eyes loved.

Liked, laughed and knew,

Under that cool sky above,

They would meet again. Anew.

The Delicate Dish of Love

Love was young in eighty two;

Its frogs legs leapt and bound.

And not a croak did pass its lips,

For true, its Prince it found.

Love felt brave in eighty three;

The rabbit chased the gun.

But then it fell and gave up chase,

For now it is black bun.

Love got lost in eighty four;

It closed its scaly eyes.

It really was a tasty dish,

But trout got second prize.

Love was lust in eighty five;

It plucked the cherry heart.

It squeezed the juice and crushed the stone,

And made a cherry tart.

Love turned sour in eighty six;

The lemon drowned the fish.

And when the fish was truly dead,

Love had lost its wish.

Two Magpies

Two magpies there abide.
Bruised hue and white,
Like foam and tide,
Ebb and flow delight.

Two magpies witness grief.
Blue and froth view
Two lovers cleave.
My tears fall.for you.

19th January 1988

THE GREEN TIGER.

Green, is the Tiger, that
From the swollen stream drinks.
It strolls, prominadely,
To its tipple place, and thinks.

Its Dandelions, Forget-me-nots,
Creeping perennials, too,
Collectively form Tiger stripes,
Whilst doused with fresh dew.

Lie shrubs, mosses and ferns
In this spinney paradigm.
This Tiger is bliss,
Yet is not what it seems.

Its legs flow from flower,
On root to the stream.
It dips in its feet,
And joins with the bream.

My feline's not real;
It roams, true enough.
But this wild cat's a coppice,
Referred to as 'Clough'.

30TH APRIL 1987.

you know. I'm bananas about you!

KNOWING...

When the colour of your love grows ~~so dim~~ dimmer
Within my eyes; and laughter saddens
Within my heart;

Did the colour of your love ~~sho~~ glow dimmer
Within my eyes? And laughter sadden
Within my heart? No! For a glimmer
Of knowing you are there, my heart gladdens.
        you're there, makes my heart gladden.

KNOWING...

Did the colour of your love glow dimmer
Within my eyes? And laughter sadden
Within my heart?
     NO! For a glimmer
Of knowing you're there, makes my heart gladden!

7 October 89.

Penny Taylor.

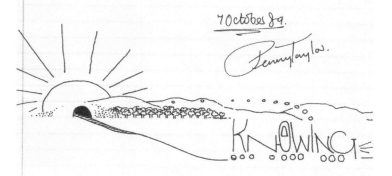

PANIC SITUATION.

Into the fire from the pan,
"Try to catch me if you can".
I'll, with reeded flute, make chords,
Guaranteed to tease your thoughts.

Unreasoned terror will rise and swell,
Making life compared to Hell.
But this, of course, reflects my name,
You've guessed it, dear; Pan, your bane!

Reply
(to a silent lover.)

Where are the secret places I shall go?
Our glade - our dell - will find my wandered soul.
For I have often been along that way -
And, in dreams, I've dreamed so fond, 'pon this day.
Oh, find me where my heart will feel at home.
Please give me time, to search... to breathe... to roam.
I've missed those lovely times within the green
Of homely hills, and wetted welcomed stream.
But, as I breathe that leafy, lingered air,
Know now that I will always... always, care.

Penny Taylor.
15 December 1989.

This was published in the Bolton Evening News, Monday February 5th 1990. and was written in reply to Mark's lovely poem he sent me post-transplant. Our love never dies.

Elevenses.

I often dream that summer heaven;
Of when our church clock struck eleven.
And see your smile — the coffee's due!
Beside that ~~chatty~~ stream we knew.
Oh Lord, I miss your cheeky grin.
A price I pay. (Immortal whim...)
But were you here, I know not now,
If I'd be strong enough to go
And leave the warmth, winging from your love...
Which binds me tighter than any glove.

Did not our parting kiss remove
The lonliness... the solitude...
Of all those years that have since passed
To prove how long our love could last?

No! Ever does this hurt remain.
(Just experience, is our gain!)
So, can two lonely hearts but ache
For ~~sweetly~~ love they both forsake?

Penny Taylor.
2nd January 1990.
11pm.

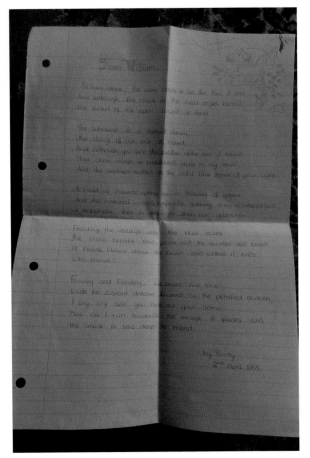

ON POETRY.

From somewhere sacred
Words spring forth.
Some dark and worshipped core.
And plip-plopped starkness
Once more reads, and
Preaches blue-lined score.

In Arts descending
Words crescend.
Inks wide voluted vine.

(An epitaph to muted tongue.
A liturgy of nib-gushed song,
And words of inner mime).

10TH FEBRUARY 1988.

A Cluster of
Dead Autumn Leaves.

When I found them, their green years had vanished.
And the clotted tear of youth remained, where
Only a mother had ever held them.

Tanned - perhaps by summers glow - they were bare,
And crisp, and bent. No beauty showed.
                          Like men
Do, they had aged, and died.
For them though, no hearts cried.

They were brothers too! - Joined by heart.
Each, stemmed, together.
            They could never part...
But within the hour when plucked from living,
Had fallen proud, and died forgiving.

Now though, from Mother Tree, each leaf was banished.

10th October 1989.
Penny Taylor.

MY PESKY COUGH.

I woke up this morning,
My backside was numb.
I'd sat up all night
And it wasnt much fun!

My lungs had run riot
Last night, around ten.
They'd bubbled, then clucked
Like a haggard old hen.

I glanced in the mirror
"Good Lord. What a sight!"
My skin was so pale
It gave me a fright.

I stood up and coughed,
And I coughed through till noon.
Then tired, it subsided,
Not a moment too soon.

I finished my neb,
Then poked at my dinner.
(With forty odd pills
I couldn't be thinner!)

A friend came at two
And we had a good chat.
Laughter was heard –
And a cough! FANCY THAT!

Tea was at six
(Finished mine around seven)
And then I could rest,
Till bed at eleven.

I lay down to sleep.
My lungs – they played up.
They gurgled and bled
So ice was then sucked.

By twelve it had settled,
Till morning I'll rest.
I pray for my transplant –
FOR THIS COUGH IS A PEST!!

4ᵗʰ Nov. 85.

Penny S Taylor.

Clock.

Clock, burning its beat into the darkness,
Carved a movement in the shadowed space.
Blankets heaved, and swelled,
Above the limbs of night.
Spines coiled, and held
The crushed pillows in dream fashioned plight.
Tick, stabbed the sharpness
Of quiet in its ebon face.

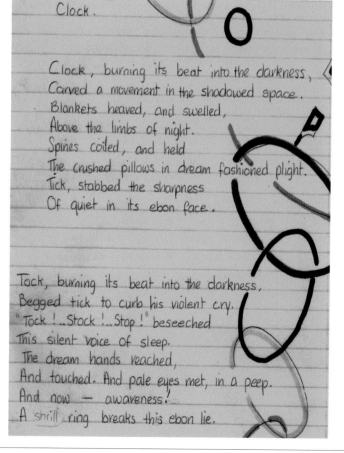

Tock, burning its beat into the darkness,
Begged tick to curb his violent cry.
"Tock!...Stock!...Stop!" beseeched
This silent voice of sleep.
The dream hands reached,
And touched. And pale eyes met, in a peep.
And now — awareness!
A shrill ring breaks this ebon lie.

Although this card is not homemade,
All Good Wishes it does Bade
For your new life in Londons bank
Where soon you'll get to know your 'rank'.

On Monday August 7ᵗʰ you'll be
Amongst a stranger company,
Where rules and regulations set –
Your first banking day, you won't forget!

But forget not also us up here,
(To whom you are a friend so dear),
And let us know just how you are; Say!
Say! Do you travel by rail, or car ?!!

Inform us of your working day –
The hours, people and the pay!
And tell us what you do at dusk –
Tea? Or on the street to busk?

And if you're homesick whilst down there,
Don't forget that we all care.
And once you find that work gets better –
Don't forget to send a letter !!

To stand upon that hill (today) tonight
Beneath pink-powdered clouds
Whilst Rose and Vetch did guard our realm
Would be a true delight.

Lying, amidst the pink-powdered clouds
in our wood, we watched the dying light.
Heaven and Earth were robed and crowned
Upon this summers night.
And Earth was pure, and rich, and well;
And Heaven found it right.

Upon our rooted thrones we sat
And leant against the back.
We whispered youthful words of love,
And slow, the sky showed dark.

Yet pink remained - a blossomed sky here -
And Earth felt pure, and crowned.
Thistle and Vetch did guard this realm;
This kingdom of love we'd found.

Heaven Sent, Taylor Made

MAGPIES ON A HILLSIDE.

I saw them today.

Two magpies on the hillside; our hillside. I stopped walking along the small, narrow path and watched them. How they flirted! Yet they seemed to be so happy, just like we were in the summer of 1985. A slight chill ran up my spine, despite the warm April breeze. Even now it hurts to remember that distant summer.

My thoughts drifted to that lovely summer day when, in a cool blue dress, I had walked past the hillside you were working on. I loved to walk through the small park so I was no stranger to the numerous trees and twisting paths, and morning is such a nice time of the day to take a liesurely walk. It prepared me for the day ahead. But nothing could have prepared me for this particular day.

At first I had ignored the wolf whistle. A group of men had stood on that hillside so I had no idea who had whistled. And I had no idea that the whistler was indeed a wolf. Perhaps there is some truth in the tale of Red Ridinghood after all. But I spoke to you didn't I, ignoring common sense. You told me how you were single and oh, would I happen to be doing anything that night? It's strange but even then there was a certain attraction between us, a certain excitememnt that only two people in love can share. Yet I knew this was absurd, we didn't even know each other. And anyway, I already had a boyfriend, so I decided not to accept your offer.

Four times I turned you down...persistant weren't you! Only when you followed me and k~~ss~~ed me did my defences fall. Only then I knew. *[kissed]*

There was a slight coldness in the breeze by the time I reached the path where you kissed me. The two magpies were close by, following me through the pathway of trees near the stream. I wondered if these were the same two magpies that followed us in 1985; I suspected they were.

I almost envy them. They are still together, still happy, sharing their love.

Yet I don't remember falling in love with you. Perhaps it was when we met...perhaps it was on one of our many country walks...or maybe it was during those times when you kissed me. We too were like those magpies though, happy yet stealing precious minutes just to be together, just to love, to kiss... Now I understand why people call these lovely birds 'thieving magpies'. For over a month we were allowed to be happy, given time to learn more about one another.

By the way, I have a job. (non payable though!) I play the Piano for the sunday school, though on the 1st week I was ½ an hour late as I'd been sat with the juniors. No·one told me for ½ hr that they already had a pianist and that I should have been with the Infants.
Luckily. I still have the Job!

This weekend will be busy as tomorrow my Uncle Ken from New Zealand and his girlfriend are coming to stay a week with us. Uncle Ken is a very, over the top, tidy person - we are not! So, it's a bit daunting for all of us having this fussy person coming to stay. If you could see my room at this minute you'd understand why I say 'daunting!'

On Saturday I'm on a stall at the Craft Fare at my old school selling (hopefully) the remainder of my books. Then, on Sunday· we have bible study at night. Fancy coming along both of you, as we are stuck for members? Still, it's only been running for 2 weeks.

Friday, the 12th, should be GREAT. I go to see the voice surgeon in Manchester who is 'eager' to get my voice done as he's only done the op. on terminally ill cancer patients & ∴ doesn't know what long term success rate is. (I may be shouting down your Telephone soon now!)

Upon our rooted thrones we sat
And leant against the back.
We whispered precious words of love;
And slow, the sky showed dark.

Yet pink remained - a blossomed hue -
And Earth felt pure, and crowned.
Thistle and vetch now geard this realm:
~~This kingdom of love we've found.~~
~~A~~ kingdom of love, unfound.
Our   renowned.
And rosy cheeks enhanced our god

Hound
w
CROWNED
SOUND
wound
wound
Sound

I said to the man at the pearly white gate,
"Hi. I got here at last. So sorry I'm late."
He frowned, scratched his beard, looked puzzled at me
Then spoke "Who are you? Have you got your own key?"
I soon shook my head for I knew I had not.
(mum's always reminded me. I always forgot!)
"I can't let you in if you don't have a key
So you'd better go back, down to Earth for your tea".
Surprised and in shock, though pleased all the same,
I looked at 'ADMISSIONS' and saw not my name.
I said to him then "Aren't my wishes all spent?
I thought that this time my last one was sent".
He laughed "No dearest child for your faith is too strong
I'm afraid you've just got your closing date wrong.
Go back, and you'll see that things start to improve.
You'll be back on your feet, and able to move".
So I turned on my heel with my heart full of hopes
And hallucinations in mind of small dancing popes!
Like the man said, I began to improve,
Slowly at first but soon I could move.
I feel I've just been through my bleakest patch ever —
Just standing up took the greatest of effort,
And it left me so breathless and gasping for air,
And I know that it gave mum and Dad such a scare.
My lungs, they felt they were closing inside —
They cramped and distressed. They caused me to cry.
Yet even to cry was impossible
I had not the breath, though I did have the will.
Oh, I cannot describe the joy I now feel
I can breathe once again and that feeling is real.
I feel I've been granted life over again.
Though why I know not. Why? Why again?

Still, it is not for me to ask why.
I'm here with a chance and I'm able to cry.
So I'll cry tears of joy and relief for my health —
I'm a millionaire with her health as her wealth.
A miracle has happened — or so it does seem —
Once more I can plan, I can walk, I can dream.
Why just yesterday I got back on my bike,
Yet two weeks ago — you should have seen what I was like!
The difference? It's steroids! Of that I feel sure,
My doctor, he's puzzled, but glad of this cure.
But thank you my friends, for you've aided his care
With your whopping big dose of Intensive Prayer.

Penny Taylor.
5th December 1991.

Above: A poem that Penny wrote to her dad's friend, Louis Morton. His reply is to the right.

Below: Louis's response to Penny's poem.
Above: The picture Louis painted. The painting is of the Cartmel chapel mentioned in the poem. Louis painted the picture and brought it to Penny's home the day after she died, not being aware of her death at the time. The chapel's door is open, and it seemed so symbolic to us all. The painting is still on the wall in Judith and John's home.

Right: John, Andrew and Louis in the Lake District following Penny's death.

Thoughts in the chapel on Cartmel Fell, and on being handed a forgotten key.

I said to the man at the old lych gate
There's a person I know who's been hit by fate,
It's strange and its weird, It's a mystery you see
Why she loves life, much more than me.
Her problems are great, but mine are not small,
I could do with more money to do up the hall,
A video recorder I would give a good home
A washing machine, two weeks in Rome.
Some jobs that I do they give me a pain
I would emigrate, I can't stand the rain.

But I've painted a picture called 'Light of the world'
Shows the faith that lights up, a bleak fell side.

I said I have faith, but it's faith in the stones
But sometimes its cold, strikes through my bones.
The roof is supported by timbers of oak
And I thought long ago, in soft word they spoke.

I said to the man who stood at the old lych gate
There's a person I know who's been hit by fate
But the poems that she writes are full to the brim
With joy and with life and a strength that's within.
"Yes I know" said the man "In your art I can see"
You paint in no people...... There lies the key
Cold stone they will press on you, your strength they will drain
But your friend has got people, to soften the pain
Her faith has got form, and the weight of your stones
And "I write of life" she calls in loud tones.

But "I thank you people" is a poem I can't write
and I stand in the shadow and envy the light.

The Babble of Bic

DEDICATED
TO
ALL
THAT I LOVE.

Thrown in, careless, amongst the rhymes
Nebulous love dominates the lines
That on each page stand bold and thick –
But alas, it's only the Babble of Bic.

Right: Penny with her book, 'The Babble of Bic'.

Middle and Bottom Left: Two pages of another book— the one that Penny created for her parents when she organised them a special anniversary holiday.

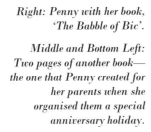

Penny was a prolific artist, writer and communicator, and it has been impossible (at times) to select precisely what should be included in this book about her life and works. I've ploughed through boxes, folders and carrier bags, and hope that what I've included will give an accurate overview of Penny's life and adequately meet Penny's request from 30-odd years ago when, aware she was dying, she asked us to publish her work and her story.

Here is 'The Babble of Bic' in which Penny refers to herself as Bic (after the pen).

She published this slim volume herself and we still have some copies available!

Our neighbor, Mrs Lee who looked after Freeway on occasion, got some of the books from our house and sold some while we were away!

Penny really enjoyed compiling her poetry and artwork for 'The Babble of Bic' and was planning to compile further of her creations into books like this one.

The title page from The Babble of Bic is at the top of this page.

The book itself is reproduced over the next few pages.

CONTENTS

DEDICATORY	3
ALPEN WOOD	6
SOUTH SEA DREAM	8
THE TRUMPET THISTLES	9
THE CHOICE	10
EMERALD DAYS	11
IN THE LAND OF NEVER END	14
THE CHEQUERED PATTERN	15
HOME	16
THE UNGATHERED FLOWER	18
THE MUTE LOVER	20
KODI AND KALI	21
WHITE COPPICE	22
MOON	24
THE ETERNAL ABSOLUTUS BETWEEN OLD EARTH AND KING THISTLE	25
LOVE	27
HEAVEN UPON THE WOLD	28
THANK YOU	31

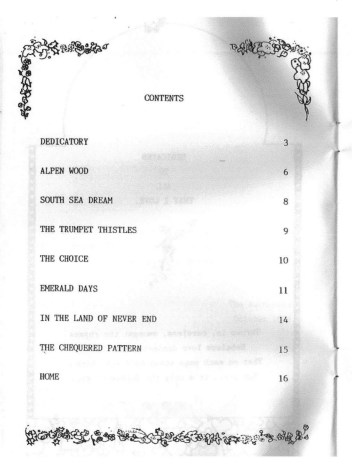

ALPEN WOOD.

Tell me about our windless wood,
And the creatures that dwell therein.
Oh, many months have passed since you
And I there laughed. We understood
Each sound, each step, of Natures whim.

    Then, our eyes met with other eyes –
Illuminated, staring skies.

    And dwelling abreast those wild few,
Whose dampened bed of leaves and grass
We shared awhile, to sit, then pass
Perhaps another hour or two,
Hushed words crept forth;

          "You know I do..."

    Your face, half cast in shadowed light,
Suddenly beamed, loving and bright.
For all that was, within that breath –
All that, which stumbled from our heart –
Unwittingly became a part
Of wooing woodlands life. And death.

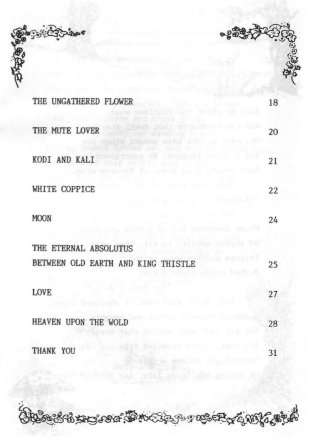

And wildness scurried past unseen;
Lost, in the magic that was ours!
Doubt not, the creatures heard our vow
And stirred the sleeping, 'pon the bough,
That every hidden eye might glean
Our dawn of love; our dawning hours.
Whilst beasts looked on; and viewed the skies;
You held me safe within your eyes.
Thus, soon our words in moonlight crept
To happy hearts.

          And fauna slept.
Silent, the voice, that moves within
Each blade of grass, each stem, each bud.

    It's many months since we did go
To our hill, where love abides. So
Tell me about our windless wood,
And the creatures that dwell therein.

(Alpen Character.)

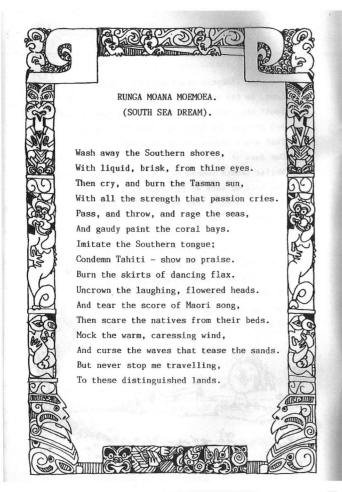

RUNGA MOANA MOEMOEA.
(SOUTH SEA DREAM).

Wash away the Southern shores,
With liquid, brisk, from thine eyes.
Then cry, and burn the Tasman sun,
With all the strength that passion cries.
Pass, and throw, and rage the seas,
And gaudy paint the coral bays.
Imitate the Southern tongue;
Condemn Tahiti - show no praise.
Burn the skirts of dancing flax.
Uncrown the laughing, flowered heads.
And tear the score of Maori song,
Then scare the natives from their beds.
Mock the warm, caressing wind,
And curse the waves that tease the sands.
But never stop me travelling,
To these distinguished lands.

THE TRUMPET THISTLES.

Where midnight love composed,
The trumpet thistles stand.
They guard our realm with dulcet tone,
Whilst purple clouds the land.

Where midnight love performed,
The trumpet thistles blare;
A flourished thorned concerto
Erupts the livid air.

At midnight loves finale
The trumpet thistles bow.
They then assume their bristled guise,
Yet no-one knows quite how.

THE CHOICE.

Suddenly, I'm here.
At lifes impending choice.
Where man does rarely stray,
To heed Creators voice.

Each day has brought me closer,
The weeks have seen me near,
To this unwanted standstill;
I step, with caution clear.

Decisions must be chosen,
And faith must not forsake.
For had Gods son not died for us,
This choice I could not make.

On deciding whether or not
to undergo heart and lung transplant
surgery. January 1988.

EMERALD DAYS.

Safe, in the sun splattered vale,
We sat and watched the grasses sail;
The bluebell breeze aroused their blade,
Sprawling seeds across the glade.

The blackie sang a spinney song,
His throaty crotchets never wrong.
And stream percussion drifted by;
Guiding, was the dragon fly.

Leading into Tigers
Clough from Ormstons
Farm.

(The 'Green
Tiger.')

Rivington Pike.

Urban gate and steps were found,
Though neglected was their sound.
Yet mans slight touch affected not
This gentle green, this gladed spot.

And whilst we sat, no need for words,
Interrupted by the birds,
We clutched the undenying grass;
The spongy, molten gold of 'Crass'.

The
Three Lakes.   Rivington.

The emerald turf cast meaningful rays,
Contentment shroud in verdant haze.
And chords continued the vintage roam.
We laughed scotch mist, then giggled home.

Up the hill from Pontis Pad,
towards Wilderswood.

IN THE LAND OF NEVER END.

There is a place called 'Never End',
Where fancies freely roam.
And dreams dwell sweet on dewy green.
And thoughts, they call it 'home'.

Its orange clouds are fruitful,
And acres yield throughout.
Rainbows paint the ceaseless bloom,
And trees grow strong and stout.

Thrashing rain is ever soft.
The sun is always glowing.
But in this charmed, eternal mind,
There breathes a sense of knowing.

For fancies flee their naked truths,
And broken dreams refuse to mend.
And thoughts are merely yesterdays,
In the land of Never End.

THE CHEQUERED PATTERN.

Only a chequered pattern remains;
A black and white ebb effigy.
Battered by seasons, hail, rain and storm.
A negative now, for all to see.

Once pictured by camera, it stood quite erect.
The smile of a blossomed abode.
Now it's encrusted by evergreen trees,
With many a tale, untold.

The roots of the lichens, the weeds and the shrubs,
Together entwine underground.
And nobody knows of their quiet interlace -
A braiding of love, unfound.

I've climbed the hill to that pattern of time,
And gazed at those tiles, whilst alone.
I've seen the true image, the developed print,
Of Lever-hulme, Lever-hume, Lever home.

The Pigeon Tower,
above the Bungalow
Grounds where Lord
Leverhulme built his home.

HOME.

Where wily winds blow warm in spring,
Blustering each flower, each tree.
Beyond the field, where blackbird sings,
Could this be home, for me?

Maybe the point where stream meets stream,
And stumbles, uncertain, to sea.
There, stones unfold. And swims the bream.
Could this be home, for me?

Safe, in the blush, of thundered clouds.
Unseen, in livid gloamings glee.
Or rainbows end, where colour crowds.
Could this be home, for me?

Where all a lovers love does flow,
(In glade, on heath, or yawning lea,)
With poppies pianissimo,
Could this be home, for me?

Encaptured in an ochre-flame,
Upon the wing of honey bee.
With every golden spark the same,
Could this be home, for me?

Forget the stream, and gust boquet.
There's a place I would rather be:
For in your arms, I'd surely say,
That this is home. For me.

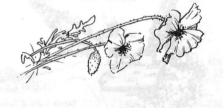

THE UNGATHERED FLOWER.

As brown washed its softness over the lake,
Lone shadows crept from the waters break.
And there, all silent in its grandeur, stood
The castle. With frail, broken clouds for its hood.

And dark. So dark, the trees stooped;
Over the shores, where the grasses drooped
Their solemn heads in quiet repose,
And kissed the bluebells chilly nose.

Replica ruins of Liverpool
Castle, built on 'Coblowe'. Rivington.

Then soft, sneezed the bluey dome;
Across the pebbled shores to roam.
Beneath each stone, rose azure mists,
Tinted with purple, and rare amethyst.

So, as the ungathered flower, lingering afar,
Shows its ghostly hue 'pon the reservoir,
A peace erupts and skims this phantom breeze;
Over the water, to the blue-mist ruins. And trees.

156

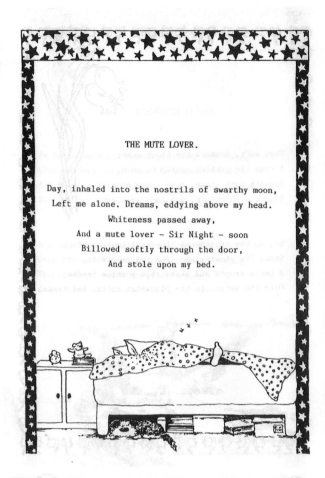

THE MUTE LOVER.

Day, inhaled into the nostrils of swarthy moon,
Left me alone. Dreams, eddying above my head.
Whiteness passed away,
And a mute lover – Sir Night – soon
Billowed softly through the door,
And stole upon my bed.

KODI AND KALI.
(SIAMESE TWINS PRESERVED IN JARS
AT GLASGOW UNIVERSITY).

Torpid life and sluggish dreams;
Rows and rows of bottled lies.
Babies screaming silent truths,
(Yet no-one heard their cries):
The cries, Oh Lord, of life and death,
And twins compressed by fate.
And horrors showed of spiritless life,
And muted faces shrieking hate.
And death was sweet compared to this –
This sideshow, mocking birth.
For death was end...finality...
And death was yet a myth.
But these immortal stifled beings,
Preserved midway the bridge of verve,
Sustained a life of passive loath –
A life they had to serve.
To treat such life like pickled prunes;
Sewed and bound like quilted down.
Is that not life in twisted view?
Or deaths abhortive frown?

WHITE COPPICE.

Somehow, I walked the long thread of those hills.
Guided, by some remote, wallowing light
That peeped from the wild skeletons of trees:

Each stood, stark!
                    Flayed, by lone winds. Peeled, by sun.
Abandoned now, where bracken soon meets night...

Parched footsteps – caught in the quietude that fills
Dying Septembers breath – hurried on;
Impatient, to welcome Octobers breeze.
But my own heavy feet – and yours – ambled,
Kicking the white dust, beneath: Which rambled,
Puffed, then scattered amongst the wayward grass.

No winds blew.
            And those hours were ours to pass...

North Bridge.
White
Coppice.

But later, light no longer peeped. Both lea
And hill were chilled.
            We drove, as darkness fell,
Past isolated farms. And I, glancing back,
Took home a lasting view: Tapered tracks
That pinch, 'pon a bend, then so suddenly
Dilate!
            And fall, onto a sheepish dell...

The Lowe, from the Cricket Ground,
White Coppice.

MOON.

There, where moon glowed clarity white,
Perceived beyond this moistened pane,
My heart beheld the quill of night
And, lovingly, inscribed your name.

So thus you glowed, with pallid moon,
Where only wonted eyes could view.
But rain quenched gloamings ink, and soon
Neither eye nor fair moon, held you.

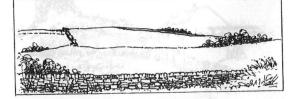

Unreluctant, I study you from my bed;
The soiled bed of Venus.
And I see you crowned by a curious buzz;
A buzzing of bees around your spinous,
                    heart stored head.

Remaining in an armoured silence,
Glancing fleetingly, nothing to say,
You sway, unspoken, amidst the sun-sprung day.
And I remain awed by your majestic presence.

Suddenly, plumage breaks above your detonated
                              heart,
And the beam-burst rays gleam your sword.
I am no longer your seasonable bawd,
For your rendering crown means Old Earth and
                    King will never part.

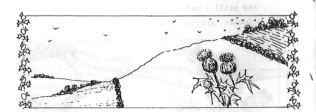

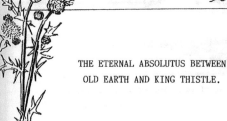

THE ETERNAL ABSOLUTUS BETWEEN
OLD EARTH AND KING THISTLE.

Silently, you lie beneath
My earthy carcass.
I wait for winter to pass,
Knowing you will rise above my wreath.

I stir, in spring, responding as you thrust,
And thrust again. Reaching high,
Pointing your way out, splintering the sky.
I, bear your weight. You, bear my trust.

And still I wait.
(Summer, arrives late).

It is immutable, as a poets words are constant.
    As hushed, as the green tiger at noon.
  It searches, as the mole, for untrodden ways.
And now, as it lingers in salty tears, or lovers bant,
    Or the rain that clouds summer, so soon,
      My love is as perpetual as the days.

HEAVEN

UPON THE WOLD.

By heck. I bet it's cold! –
Where the ruddiness is flung,
Above our hill.

      Grasses, dizzying, green and gold.
Dizzy. And dizzy. – No thought, or care.
And beasts; imparting their rich dung
To a richer earth.

      – Oh, that I were there!
To witness in those windless veins
Of thorn, and tangled undergrowth,
The warm, bewhiskered creatures, still
In sleep. Upon our hill.
And gleaming star of Bethlehem –
Weaving, splendid, down the lanes.
Pale-petalled in the eyes of men,
Yet, to an insect – jewelled! And both
The farmers dogs are barking; loudly
Now, in iteration.

      Loud. Into the night,..

And oft, the golden crops in dream,
Breathe, and scatter, beside the stream.
And winds, in rare tempestuous fun,
Tickle the ears of corn. And run!
Approaches morning – over the stile.
And cows – conducted through the gate,
Into the field in single file –
Slowly munch the grass. And wait.
Accustomed now, the tranquil air.
But lo! The butterfly intrudes.
Say. Does its liquid colour stare
And flutter, still, in pulchritude?

I wish that I were there...

Lying, afresh, with giddy grasses.
Waving to cumulus,

      as slow....it passes.
Surely it's heaven, upon the wold.
But, by heck. I bet ... I bet it's cold!

30

And glowing, scarlet,
Vastness treads. And proudly
Rests the dawning light.
Rain clouds blowing fluently;
The hill – all mud liquidity.
Oh. Night and the dawn have met.

Yes. Clearly, I see, where they meet –
Quiescent, the trembled land. Replete,
The dallying breeze:

      Those whisps, a loitering tease...

THANK YOU.

How many times within a day
Do I sit down and gently pray,
For all those things that You might give
To help me breathe, to help me live?
Though never, do I ask for much –
Just that your caring hands might touch.
And give me strength, Oh Lord I pray,
To guide me through another day.
And then when I, with healthy smile,
Succeed in running five long miles,
Please let me not forget your touch,
That I might thank you, very much.

31

Appendix 3: Photographs and Memories
Gallery of Judith's Artwork

Above: Judith's painting of Nook Farm, Harwood, where she used to live. The painting shows Judith's granddad and his horse. Jack.

*Some of Judith's own artwork.
Left: Freeway. Right: Tramp.*

The ginger cat is Kelly, the family cat from when Penny was a child. It used to boss over poor Tramp the dog!

Gallery of John's Artwork

Some of John's artwork.

Displayed here are pages from some of John's art notebooks, many dating back to when he studied art in the 1960s.

Far left: Judith's parents.

Left: Penny, with Judith's mum.

Penny with her Auntie Betty and Uncle Dave from Scotland.

Below Left: John's parents, John and Vera.

Penny with her dad at John's parents. And above with Tramp, the dog.

Bottom Left: Brian and Chris, good friends who did a lot for all the family.

Above Left: Penny aged about 9, with Juliet, Michele and another friend at a St John's Church. Juliet and Penny used to pretend to put plays on, using the Taylor's window as a theatrical stage and curtain.
Above Right: Penny with Michele fishing in Clitheroe.

Penny's cousins Helen, Catherine and John.

Judith's sister, Barbara and family with Penny.

Fun-loving Penny with her mum and dad.

Penny and her class at Horwich Parish Primary School. Penny is third from the left on the middle row.

Judith's niece, Helen, with Penny in Rivington.

John Taylor, John Duckworth and Penny on the moors near home with a Rivington Pike view. This would have been taken on Good Friday, when locals climb the Pike—see the masses of cars and vans in the background!

Catherine Pollitt (Penny's cousin) who stayed with us for Christmas 1975. This photo was taken at John's mum and dad's on Chorley New Road.

Penny and Deborah on holiday.

Above: At a Cystic Fibrosis charity event with the Mayor and Mayoress. Penny was about eleven years old and loved French Fancies. At this event she saw a large plate of mixed cakes on the table, and took ALL the French Fancies!

Two photos of Penny and Deborah on holiday in the Lake District, posing.

Penny with Judith and Michele in the Isle of Man.

Heaven Sent, Taylor Made

Below, Left and Right: Penny with dad and friends, and with Dr Ellis, Freeway and the doctor's own dogs.

Above: Auntie Margaret would make amazing cakes!

Above: Penny and John Duckworth on John's 18th.

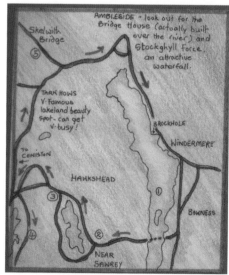

Above and Right: Just a couple of illustrations from the scrapbook Penny created for her parents when she bought them both a holiday in the Lake District.

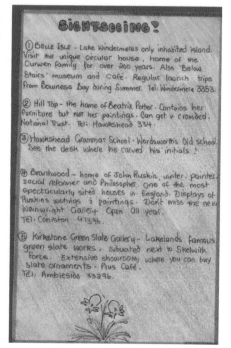

Above: Penny with her Auntie Betty and Uncle Dave from Scotland.

Monsall Outpatients.

Penny hard at work at the dining table.

Below: Mark Burgess, another attendee, and Andrew Morley sitting on a pavement at a CF conference. Also, Andrew Morley and Penny singing.

Penny and John Duckworth, and his mum, Kath.

Above: Norah, Judith's old friend, would often help out. She would bring Susie to play with Penny, and did a lot for Penny and the family.

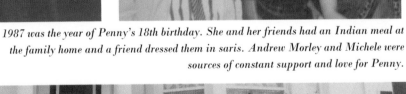

Penny and Lesley all grown up. This is the last photo of the two friends as Lesley now lives in Australia. She moved there in 1990.

1987 was the year of Penny's 18th birthday. She and her friends had an Indian meal at the family home and a friend dressed them in saris. Andrew Morley and Michele were sources of constant support and love for Penny.

At a Cystic Fibrosis Conference in Solihull. Penny, her friend Mark, and Andrew Morley attended.

Above: Penny and Freeway in Rivington.

Above: With Princess Alexandra at a CF reception in Claridges in London.

Cousin Roy and Anne McBurnie in Glasgow. They were friends to us and were great sources of support since Penny was young. Other photos above are all from Scotland trips to visit Veronica and other family members.

Right: Our friends, Cath and Les.

Above: Dr Dickson and Penny at home after her transplant.

Above: The Taylor family cycling in Rivington, on Penny's final bike ride. She had an oxygen cylinder attached to the back of her bike.

Above: Penny with Megan and with Michele.

Right: Michael, Helen (Penny's cousin) and Penny.

Above: A family photo. John Taylor, niece Helen, nephew's wife Helen, niece's husband Michael, Andrew (Cath's husband), Judith, nephew John, Judith's sister Barbara, niece Catherine and brother in law, Stan. Penny always enjoyed seeing her family.

Left: A selection of Penny's medals. Right: Not the greatest photo, but a special one as this was the last holiday the four of us had—in Derbyshire. With John, Judith, Andrew Morley and Penny.

Above: Paul and Joanne, and their parents Fay and Graham McGinn. Fay was at college with Judith and used to come and support us and Penny.

Above: Anita with Anne Brownlow who is holding Anita's grandchild, Jessica. Anita knew Penny through Judith's church fellowship group. Anne did a lot for Penny and still visits her grave every week.

Above: Our niece Helen, Judith, John and Penny.

Right: Penny's drugs from around the time she was being treated for tuberculosis.

Above: Penny at the wedding of Judith's nephew, John, at his wedding to Helen (author of Ambassadress Angel earlier in the book.

Above: Penny as bridesmaid for her friend, Sharon.

Left: Penny as a bridesmaid for Judith's niece, Helen.

Below: With Sarah.

Left: The first post-transplant picture of Penny and her mum and dad, when they first came home from Papworth. Penny had been getting out and about a lot at this stage and was loving life.

Above: Penny on her final holiday with her mum at Grasmere in the Lake District. Penny is wearing her mum's coat and looks well and healthy owing to the steroids and other drugs she was taking.

Left: A selection of Penny's cards at Papworth following her transplant.

Conclusion

The final photo of the three of us together. This was Penny on her 22nd birthday in June 1988. In the September, they had to operate to remove part of her transplanted lung, and Penny quickly went downhill after that, passing away in January 1992.

In writing this book, my aim was to tell the story of our daughter, Penny, and to show how her faith, positive outlook on life and sense of humour helped and supported her throughout her life. I hope that others who find themselves in a similar situation to our family will gain some encouragement from reading about Penny. Her love of life and the recording of her own life through words and art give an insight into Penny's thoughts about her condition and about her personality too. We hope you've enjoyed Penny's poems, pictures and writings. I hope you'll also share the laughter and the tears which we all shared. Although Penny died aged only twenty-two, she filled her years with fun, love, laughter and a deep understanding of her faith. I have now shared Penny's twenty-two years with you.

Penny and John followed Penny's instructions and got on their bikes after her death. They are pictured here at St Andrews in Scotland while staying at Judith's cousin's house.

A collage of memories of Penny, her friends and family members.

Nights Driving ~~coming~~ back from Papworth with Penny when we were both tired after a long day, we would put a ~~tape~~ of Abba on or Simon & Garfunkel, which we both loved and to keep me awake whilst driving, Penny would often fall asleep as worn out with lung funtion & other tests throughout the day.

Today ~~to~~ whenever these songs are played it takes me back ~~to~~ ~~times of happy~~ to coming home in the car with Penny, ~~even now~~ 30yrs later it makes me sad that we are no longer ~~going~~ coming & going to Papworth and brings tears flowing, Music of all kinds brings memories of the past happy & sad

Judith Would Like To Thank...

Samantha Davies

We met Sam when she was fourteen years of age, after Penny had died. Penny had always wanted to write a book about her life and friends, but she didn't have the time before she died, and when she was in her final days she asked us if we would try to write it. She told us that all the material was there, but it just needed compiling into a book. That was all very well, but I couldn't type, so eleven years ago Sam offered to type it out for me, so I said what I wanted to say, and Sam typed my words onto John's computer. After the first chapter Sam was unable to continue and I found it too daunting on my own, but Sam is a good friend to this day.

Janet Marks

Janet met Penny and family at the church's fellowship group. Janet encouraged Judith to work towards getting this book completed.

Kath Worthington

Kath has been a close friend for over fifty years, and for most of Penny's life she helped whenever she could. Nothing is ever too much trouble for her. Kath has helped me by proofreading my book as I wrote it. She spent hours going through Penny's letters to select relevant material from the hundreds of letters sent to Penny over the years (and many of her replies to them).

Dorothy Lee

We had known Dorothy since before Penny was born as we lived a few doors away from each other. She was pregnant at the same time I was, and she had a son, Timothy. John was Timothy's Godfather and Dorothy was Penny's Godmother. For a few years Penny and Timothy grew up together. Dorothy, David and Tim then moved to a new house about a mile away and we didn't see as much of each other for a little while. A few years ago, Dorothy's husband, David, passed away, and one day I was talking to her about 'the book' I was writing and she offered to assist. She did so, and also assisted by talking through Penny's life to help us put the story together.

Judith Would Like To Thank...

John Taylor, Penny's dad and my husband

I couldn't have picked a worse time to create this book because throughout the entire period we were having alterations done to our house, and things were in a terrible mess. It was a difficult process at times to do the book, even without contending with this upheaval, but it was also very uplifting to see in Penny's work the faith, positivity and humour which had given her the strength to cope.

But John found the process very difficult. Even though he had started writing this book himself he found that it was too upsetting to plough through the masses of Penny's material. As time went on I was asked to think of a title, but it was John who came up with 'Heaven Sent, Taylor Made' and that to me sums it all up.

Lesley Atherton, Publisher

I met Judith in early 2019, shortly after setting up my publishing company, Scott Martin Productions. The process of putting this book together has been a challenging one, to say the least. The sheer volume of information which required compiling and laying out, made it a very long term project ! It's been a privilege to be so involved in this mammoth and useful project, though there were times when I wondered if I'd see it through. Judith recently reminded me of one visit I made to her home when I told her 'If I didn't like you, I would have packed it in way before now'!
I'm so pleased that Judith has been able to see the publication of a book that would have made Penny very proud.

Mark Burgess Friend

Thanks also go to Mark Burgess for providing a little of his story and especially for the back cover of this book.

The rainbow and butterflies were very appropriate.

Printed in Great Britain
by Amazon